THE STARS

Ann Arbor
Science
Library

THE STARS

by W. Kruse and W. Dieckvoss

ANN ARBOR

THE UNIVERSITY OF MICHIGAN PRESS

Contents

INTRODUCTION

This book deals with the stars: the "countless" stars we can see in the sky at night and the many others we cannot see with the naked eye.

It assumes that the reader does not take the same view of the heavens as his ancestors did thousands of years ago, or as his contemporaries do in darkest Africa. He knows that there is a multitude of "fixed stars" which remain year after year in unchanging constellations, and that there are other heavenly bodies which carry out lively and varied movements.

We are not concerned here with our immediate family —the moon that circles the earth, or the planets and comets that move around the sun. Even our beautiful indispensable sun is mentioned only because it is one of the millions of stars in cosmic space.

Will enough be left to fill a whole book? The question is not foolish. Only fifty years ago, the exclusion of the sun and the solar system would not have left us much to talk about. But there has been a great change since then. Large telescopes, built since the turn of the century, have opened the way to the vast spaces of the universe. At the same time, the advance of physics has enabled us to understand the language of light, the language in which we receive all our communications from the world of the stars. This expansion of astronomy beyond the solar system has been rapid and intense. Today the greater part of astronomical activity deals with the stars.

We cannot but be attracted by this great new field of scientific inquiry. But this new science, born of the most recent theoretical and technical developments—is it not perhaps so complicated that no one but a specialist can understand it? Fortunately, not so. The basic principles which have led to the most important discoveries concerning the stars are for the most part perfectly understandable—sometimes even surprisingly simple. The practical workings of the new methods are, of course, far from simple; they presuppose a thorough knowledge of modern mathematics, physics, and practical astronomy. But we can leave those things to the specialists, casting a glance at their technical activities only when it begins to look as though the astronomers were having it too easy. We can try to get a bird's-eye view of the methods by which they arrive at their impressive and sometimes strange findings. Once we know something about the methods, perhaps the results will seem a little less amazing and also a good deal more credible.

The Goal

To begin with, we must leave aside the awe and wonder we feel when we look upon the starry sky in all its glory and adopt instead the sober attitude of the astronomer. The astronomer asks questions—and if there is no ready answer, he seeks it in the sky with the scientific and technical equipment of his times.

What do we see when, in this frame of mind, we stand beneath the dark dome of the sky? Assume that we can get away from the glow of the city and have an unobstructed view of the whole heaven. There is a deep, black darkness above us out of which shine vast multitudes of lights. They are not all equally bright; we see at once that there are many more faint lights than bright lights. Nor are they arranged in a very orderly fashion. Still, many of them form striking patterns that are easy to remember. These are the constellations, most of which have since ancient times borne the names of mythological men and beasts. Most of us no longer recognize their pictures in the stars. We see only geometric figures which do not account for the names, but which can easily be recognized as constellations.

Without giving it much thought, we have just made use of an important bit of knowledge. If we can group the stars into constellations that we can remember, it means that they must always appear, or recur, in this way. And this is in fact the case. Night after night, year after year, we see the same figures in the sky. They are today as they were described centuries ago.

Yet the stars do not stand still. If we take a little time, we observe that new stars appear in the east, others vanish in the west. It is as though a black sphere studded with glittering dots were turning round an axis that runs through the polestar. For thousands of years man thought that this was actually so. It has taken us a long time and much effort to find out that the earth is a merry-go-round which makes the stars seem to spin around us.

We know, then, that the sky is not a planetarium but only looks like one. What we see is not a spherical shell, but immeasurable, dark space in which the stars are placed seemingly side by side, but actually at greatly varying distances from us. Our earth is afloat in this space which extends in all directions, interspersed with glittering stars, so that if for a moment we forget what space really is we see it as a dome studded with lights. The same illusion could happen to us on earth. After dark, when the lights are on, we may look down from a hill or mountaintop upon a thickly settled countryside and get a very similar impression. Again there is a network of luminous points studding the darkness. Yet we would never imagine that we are looking at a wall with lights on it. We know what these lights mean and how they are spaced.

We do not know as much about the stars. What are they and what do they mean? At least, we can form a plausible opinion. We know a good many things about our sun. Anyone can see that it is round like a plate. But we do not think of it as a plate, but as a ball hovering in space like the ball that is the earth. If we follow the spots that appear on the sun from time to time, we can even see that it turns, like the earth.

Seen from the earth, the sun seems to be a rather large disk. But if we were able to move away from it, that disk would grow smaller and smaller and finally shrink to a mere point of light: it would look like a star. This fact can be observed right here on earth: a light bulb, obviously spherical when examined close at hand, becomes a luminous point when seen from a distance of a few miles. Thus, we have good reason to suppose that the stars are luminous spheres. True, we can offer no concrete proof. Any spyglass is strong enough to show that a luminous point in the countryside is a light bulb. But even the largest telescope cannot do as much for the stars; they remain points.

The mere thought of the sky as space interspersed with stars suggests a host of questions. It is not enough to know that the stars are floating in space—we also want to know where they are, how far away, whether there are stars everywhere in space, and whether they are evenly distributed in all the regions of space. And if we knew all this, we would go on to ask whether they all remain in their places, as it would seem from the unchanging appearance of the sky—or whether they are moving, just as the earth, the moon, and the other members of the solar system are moving. Could there be connections and relations between these luminous spheres?

What about their size? What are they made of, and what makes them send out light?

As we seek the answers to these questions, new questions will spring up. And the last and most difficult question of all, which we are bound to meet no matter where we start, is the question of the whence and whither, the past and future of the universe.

This is our task. It is now time to look at what tools we have, and what has been accomplished so far.

PART ONE: *Ways to the Stars*

The Language of the Universe

We know full well that our earth is a tiny speck floating in a vast universe that we have no means of leaving. Yet we set out to investigate the remotest parts of
that universe, much as we investigate our own surroundings. This undertaking seems all the more daring when
we consider how narrow a bridge connects us with the
stars.

Leaving aside what we have learned and curbing our
imagination, what do we actually see as we stand under
the open night sky? Light shines into our eyes from various directions—and that is all. Light is the bridge between us and the stars. ("Light" should be taken in general terms as an undulatory radiation—which includes
such phenomena as radio waves. Of this more on p. 96.)
The other things that come to us from outer space—
meteors and particles of cosmic radiation—give us no
direct knowledge of the stars. Therefore, if we can find
out anything at all about them, it will have to be by in-
terpreting their light.

At first, the attempt to learn much by this one means
may not look too promising. But, luckily, the language
of light is very rich. The deeper we penetrate into its
subtleties, the more we learn about those remote realms
that are otherwise inaccessible to us.

What we might call the everyday language of light is
perfectly familiar from daily experience. We know that a

light bulb hanging in the middle of a room can be seen from all sides, and from above and below, as long as it is not screened in some way. The light shines from the bulb in all directions. It spreads in rays that travel in a straight line, as we can see by placing a pencil on the table and looking at its shadow. In the room, it may not be so evident that the light impression we receive grows fainter as we move away from the source of light. But there is no doubt about it—a street lamp half a mile away does not look as bright as the lamp in front of our house. If we wanted to take the trouble, we could determine just how much fainter it looks. But the same result can be had more easily by a little experiment (Fig. 1).

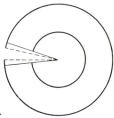

FIG. 1. Propagation of light.

We punch a hole in a sheet of black paper and hold it up to the light. When the distance between the hole and the source of light is doubled, only one-fourth as much light shines through it. Now we do not go about with a punched piece of black paper before our eyes— nor do we have to, for we already see the world through an opening, or rather two openings: our pupils. We look at the same lamp first from a distance of 10 feet, then from a distance of 100 feet—only $\frac{1}{100}$ as much light will shine through our pupil in the second case as in the first. This may not be quite true because our pupil expands or contracts automatically as the light grows fainter or brighter. But it does hold true for a telescope, because its "pupil" does not change automatically. If we look through the same telescope at two equally bright stars, one of them twice as far away as the other, the nearer one will cast $2 \times 2 = 4$ times as much light into our telescope. This simple law of light propagation will prove extremely useful.

The Telescope

A good many people take it for granted that telescopes are used because they allow us to see everything bigger. This idea is not false, but it does not strike at the heart of the question.

What do we ordinarily do when we wish to examine an object more closely? We move our eye closer to it (Fig. 2) in order to see it at a large angle, so that its image in our eye will cover as much of our retina as possible. But we cannot go on coming closer indefinitely. If we get closer than the limit of distinct vision (about 10 inches), we no longer can see clearly. We then help

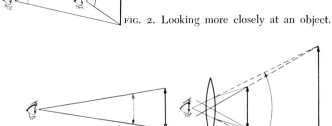

FIG. 2. Looking more closely at an object.

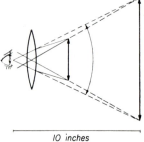

10 inches	10 inches

FIG. 3. A lens used as a magnifying glass.

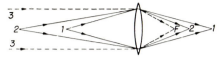

FIG. 4. A lens as a telescope objective: re-producing points on the axis.

ourselves with a magnifying glass which, if held correctly, has the effect shown in Figure 3. The effect of the lens is that we no longer see the small object but a magnified (and actually nonexistent) image, which has the additional advantage of being properly placed in relation to our eye.

What good does that do us with the stars? The difficulty with them is precisely that we cannot move closer to them. But can we bring the stars closer to us? This is the purpose of the telescope. Its essential part is also a lens—in actual telescopes, a system of at least two and usually three or more lenses which work together like an ideal converging lens. Such a lens projects images that actually exist, "real" images, of objects that are far enough away. Every camera is a small telescope; it captures the real image on the photographic plate, the same image we can see in the ground-glass viewer.

How does the telescope produce that image? Suppose a luminous point, the short filament of a flashlight bulb for example, casts a bundle of light rays on a telescopic object glass (Fig. 4). Behind the lens, the rays will again form a bundle which narrows down to a point and then spreads out again. We hold a sheet of paper directly behind the lens in the path of the bundle of light. On it there appears a bright circle which grows smaller and brighter as we move the paper away from the lens. At a certain distance the circle shrinks to a very bright point. Farther on, it grows larger and fainter again. At the tip of the cone of rays, the shining point reappears again as

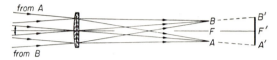

FIG. 5. A lens as a telescope objective: reproducing points situated to the side.

a point, and since every point in a real object is at this distance reproduced as a point, the object is copied point for point: a real image is produced.

In the interest of simplicity let us deal with just one luminous point. Where its image is produced depends on its distance from the lens. The farther away it is moved, the closer its image comes to the point F where all the rays emitted by an "infinitely" distant point come together. Why this point F is called "focus," which means hearth or fireplace, we can find out by means of the rays of the sun.

At this distance, an image arises even if the rays are not parallel to the axis of the telescope but strike it at an angle (Fig. 5). In this case the image is not on the axis, but at the point where the ray that passes through the center and suffers no refraction strikes the focal plane. It is easy to see that the distance of the image point from the axis depends on the angle that the incoming ray forms with the axis. If we assume an angle of 3° and a focal length of 80 inches, the distance between the images would be 4 inches. (The focal length depends on the curvature of the lens surfaces.) This would also be the distance between the images of two stars that are 3° distant from each other in the sky.

The same calculation holds if we take as our objects two points, one at the upper and one at the lower edge of the moon. The angle at which the disk of the moon appears measures $\frac{1}{2}$°; in our telescope, accordingly, the moon has a diameter of 0.7 inch. A telescope with a focal length of 800 inches provides an image of the moon 7 inches in diameter—quite a fair size.

Even this image is much smaller than the moon itself. The moon cannot be said to be "magnified" by the telescope. And yet the image with its diameter of 7 inches gives us pause: it looks bigger than the real moon. To clear up this confusion, we need only remember our earlier observation that the size of the image depends on the angle at which we look at an object. When we look at our large photograph of the moon from the usual distance of 10 inches it appears to us at an angle of 40°, 80 times larger than the natural moon, and even the image of the moon in our telescope with the 80-inch focal length is in this sense 8 times as large as the moon in the sky.

If we think this matter through carefully we recognize the true importance of the telescope: *the real image replaces the object.* We now have the photographic image black on white, can take it home, and examine it in the greatest detail with a magnifying glass or, better still, a microscope. We can measure with a ruler the distances from one point on the picture to another. This is most convenient and, if the measurements are made with a microscopic scale, much more accurate than any measurements made with a goniometer (an instrument for measuring angles) pointed at the sky.

Measurements can be taken even without making a photograph. Standing behind the focus, where the bundle of rays spreads out, we see the image of the moon, for example, exactly as if it were before us on a photographic plate. Armed with a magnifying glass, we can come closer to it so as to see it larger. If we build our magnifying glass, or a system of several lenses, into the telescope in the form of an eyepiece close behind the focus, we have the usual "visual" telescope. We can add to it further by introducing a measuring apparatus, a micrometer, close to the focal plane. Now we can measure our images just like photographic plates.

The upshot of it all is that the telescope actually allows us to see distant objects larger and with greater precision. Through the telescope, sun and moon appear considerably larger than to the naked eye, and the planets, which to the naked eye are indistinguishable from the fixed stars, become clearly recognizable disks. But when we hopefully direct our telescope at a bright star we are in for a disappointment. Even in the telescope the star is only a point of light, and it will not grow larger no matter how powerful an eyepiece we use. The explanation is simple. The real image projected by the object glass of the telescope grows smaller with increasing distance, and if the distance is very great, the object shrinks to a point of which even the strongest eyepiece cannot make a surface. All the telescope seems to tell us about the stars is that if they are as large as the moon, the planets, or even our sun, they must be exceedingly far away.

In fact, we learn a great many other things by the use of the telescope. An experiment will show how. We take a sheet of opaque paper and punch a number of holes in it. The smallest should be about the size of a pinhead, the largest about as big as a penny. We hold the paper close to one eye and look through one hole after another at a light bulb. The bulb will vary greatly in brightness. It will look the least bright through the smallest hole. As the hole grows larger, the brightness increases, since more light enters our eye through the larger hole. Unfortunately, we find that the largest holes do us no good; once they have reached a certain size the lamp does not grow brighter. The reason, obviously, is the size of our own pupil: light in excess of what our pupil will admit can produce no effect in our eye.

If lenses did not have the power to produce real images, we should have no clearer impression of the stars than we can get with the naked eye. We cannot, after all, bring the stars closer. But since we can bring our pupil close to the focal point where all the light gathered by the object glass comes together, we are able to take a much larger amount of light into our eye (Fig. 6). The larger the opening of the telescope, the brighter the stars will appear to us. This would not be too important for the stars we can see with the naked eye. But in using telescopes we soon notice that there are other stars, in fact very many of them, whose light is so feeble that the thin bundle of rays which passes through our unaided pupil is not sufficient to make an impression. To see all these stars, as well as others invisible for other reasons, we build larger and larger telescopes with the largest possible openings.

In this race for light, reflecting telescopes have the advantage over refractors. Everything we have accomplished so far with lenses can also be done with concave mirrors. Thus, there are two basic types of astronomical telescopes: refractors—lenses that refract, or bend, the light rays; and reflectors—mirrors that send them back. The single surface on which the whole effectiveness of the reflector depends is easier to manufacture in large sizes than the at least four surfaces required for the great refractors, and the glass need not be so uniform

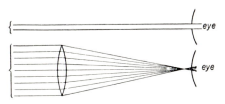

FIG. 6. The object glass as a "catcher" of light.

and free of flaws, since only the reflecting surface matters. Thus, there are reflectors with mirrors up to 200 inches in diameter (Mt. Palomar in California)—but the 40-inch Yerkes refractor, built in 1900, remains the largest in existence. A further advantage of the reflector is that the coating of silver or aluminum with which the concave surface of the mirror is covered reflects nearly all

FIG. 7. Lippert astrograph of the Hamburg Observatory in Hamburg-Bergedorf. Three photographic telescopes with different types of optical arrangement and two visual guiding telescopes are combined into one instrument.

FIG. 8. Inauguration of the 200-inch reflector on Mt. Palomar.

the light that falls on it, while in and between the lenses of the great objectives 30 to 40 per cent of the light is lost by absorption and reflection.

Unfortunately, the mirror, too, has its weakness: it gives sharp images only of objects toward which its axis points. In sky photographs made with reflectors, the stars are sharp points only in the center; toward the edge of the plate they are "comets" (Fig. 82). For the measurement of celestial photographs, this disadvantage is serious, but for many other purposes the amount of light is the main factor. About twenty years ago, it became possible to overcome this weakness of reflector telescopes. When a very thin, specially ground lens is used in conjunction with a mirror, very little light is lost and a sharp image is obtained even at some distance from the center (Fig. 11). The Schmidt telescope based on this principle has proved extremely useful. Photographed with this type of telescope, the stars show up amazingly sharp to the very edge of the plate. Schmidt telescopes are twice as long as ordinary telescopes, or even as common reflectors of the same focal length, because the thin lens, known as the correcting plate, must be placed at a distance from the reflecting mirror. The photographic plate or film also has to be curved, so that the image falls on a suitable spherical surface. Despite these two drawbacks, the sharpness of the images obtained with the Schmidt telescope represents such a great advantage that instruments of this type are constantly being built.

The largest Schmidt telescope is that at Mt. Palomar Observatory (Fig. 9). Its reflector has a diameter of 72 inches, its aperture measures 48 inches. It is an indispensable companion to the 200-inch reflector, because the large celestial field it can photograph all at once enables it to find the objects which its big brother will then examine in detail.

Telescopes may be classified in other ways. There are "visual" and "photographic" telescopes. Both types are still in use, although the photographic method of observation has become predominant. It produces pictures that are available at all times, to be examined as often as we please. This allows us to crowd a maximum of observation into the few precious hours suitable for the purpose, and to use other hours or other personnel for the time-consuming elaboration of observations. Photographs, moreover, give information about a good many things that the eye cannot see even through large tele-

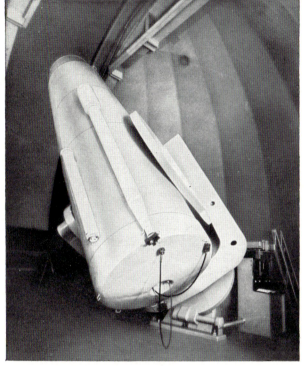

FIG. 9. The big Schmidt telescope on Mt. Palomar.

scopes. The eye is more sensitive to momentary impressions than any photographic plate. But the photographic impression increases with the time of exposure—the photographic plate "stores up" light, and this the eye cannot do.

There are many other considerations that determine the form of our telescopes. The optical or mechanical parts must be adapted to the special job they are meant to do. As a result, a large observatory is a veritable arsenal of optical cannon of the most diverse models and calibers.

The recently developed "radio telescopes" (Fig. 10) look entirely different from our customary telescopes. We use them to catch radio waves coming from outer space. Any powerful radio receiving set with a proper antenna can do as much. When we are listening to the radio, waves from space are merely interference. In order to study this interference in itself, we must surround our antenna with great metallic mirrors, which allow us to pick up rays coming from any direction we choose. Whole mirrors are not needed. Nets suffice, but they must be large to be effective. The resulting installations are enormous.

A Glance Around the Sky

The sky that these great artificial eyes open up to us is far more magnificent and mysterious than the natural sky. We do not need a large telescope to be convinced. Figure 11 shows a section of the heavens close to Deneb,

FIG. 10. A radio telescope at the Leiden Observatory.

FIG. 11. The Milky Way in Cygnus with the American nebula (so called because of its shape). This photograph was made with the 14-inch Schmidt telescope of the Hamburg Observatory.

the brightest star in the constellation of Cygnus. With the naked eye we could see only a dozen stars in this patch of sky. We do not, to be sure, find such an abundance of stars all over the sky. I have selected a field in the Milky Way to make the contrast particularly striking. It gives us an idea of the nature of this luminous belt that runs round the sky.

For the moment, we shall do what men have done through the centuries since the invention of the telescope: let our eyes wander over the heavens. A good many things stand out from the general sea of stars.

FIG. 12. A group of clusters in Auriga (Lippert astrograph, Hamburg Observatory).

FIG. 13. The globular star cluster Omega Centauri (Victoria telescope of the Cape Town Observatory).

There are places where a great quantity of stars are clustered together, and indeed we call such swarms of stars *clusters* (Fig. 12). We notice the distinctly spherical shape of the cluster in Figure 13. In Figure 14 we see something entirely different: a great luminous cloud with blurred outlines. These formations we call *nebulae*, from the Latin word for mist. Their glow is not the merging light of many stars, as with the Milky Way; they really are "mists," though much more diffuse than our mists and clouds. Formations such as we see in Figure 15 also go by the name of nebulae, although they are not nebulae but stellar systems floating in space (a fact which was not known at the time when this term was first applied to them). Because of their spiral-like appearance, they are called spiral nebulae or simply spirals. Spirals are

FIG. 14. The largest of the approximately 150 ring-shaped gaseous nebulae; it lies in Aquarius and has an apparent size of roughly one-fourth the full moon (36-inch reflector of the Lick Observatory in California).

FIG. 15. An unusually distinct spiral nebula in the constellation Pisces (39-inch reflector of the Hamburg Observatory).

perhaps the most remarkable and interesting objects in the sky. There are millions of them, and it is certain that they hold an important place in the structure of the universe. The road to the full knowledge of their significance was long, and not always straight. I shall deal with them only after thorough preparation.

I. DIRECTION
(CELESTIAL POSITION)

Mapping the Stars

If we wish to study them seriously we must first of all put some order into the swarm of stars. It can be done— witness the fact that for thousands of years the bright stars have been grouped into constellations. To the naked eye the position of the stars in relation to one another is unchanging, and if we mark them down on charts one by one and give them names, we can tell them apart and talk about them. Proper names, however, are today used only for the brightest stars; the others are designated by Greek letters (α, β, γ, δ . . . , alpha, beta, gamma, delta . . .) and the names of the constellations to which

Names and Astronomical Designations of the Best-Known Stars

NAME	BRIGHTNESS IN MAGNITUDES (SEE P. 61)	ASTRONOMICAL DESIGNATION
Polaris (the Polestar)	2.1	alpha Ursae Minoris (in the Little Dipper or Little Bear)
Achernar	0.6	alpha Eridani (in Eridanus)
Mira	(p. 78)	omicron Ceti (in Cetus)
Algol	2.1–3.2	beta Persei (in Perseus)
Algenib	1.9	alpha Persei (in Perseus)
Aldebaran	1.1	alpha Tauri (in Taurus)
Capella	0.2	alpha Aurigae (in Auriga)
Rigel	0.3	beta Orionis (in Orion)
Betelgeuse	0.9	alpha Orionis (in Orion)
Canopus	−0.9	alpha Carinae (alpha Argus) (in Argo)
Sirius (the Dog Star)	−1.6	alpha Canis Majoris (in Canis Major)
Castor	2.0	alpha Geminorum (in Gemini)
Pollux	1.2	beta Geminorum (in Gemini)
Procyon	0.5	alpha Canis Minoris (in Canis Minor)
Regulus	1.3	alpha Leonis (in Leo)
Mizar	2.2	zeta Ursae Majoris (in the Big Dipper or Great Bear)
Alcor	4.0	g Ursae Majoris (in the Big Dipper)
Spica	1.2	alpha Virginis (in Virgo)
Arcturus	0.2	alpha Boötis (in Boötes)
Gemma	2.3	alpha Coronae Borealis (in Corona Borealis)
Antares	1.2	alpha Scorpii (in Scorpio)
Vega	0.1	alpha Lyrae (in Lyra)
Altair	0.9	alpha Aquilae (in Aquila)
Deneb	1.3	alpha Cygni (in Cygnus)
Fomalhaut	1.3	alpha Piscis Australis (in Piscis Australis)

they belong. The alphabetical order usually indicates the order of brightness.

There are still other designations, such as Roman letters (like the *g* in the designation of Alcor) and numbers. But all such indications prove inadequate to list the fainter stars that have become visible through the telescope. We must cast about for another method. Why not simply do what the geographers have done to designate points on the surface of our earth? The earth is a sphere, and the sky appears as a sphere. We ought to be able to use very similar methods. To say that one star belongs to the Big Dipper and another to Orion, it is pretty much the same as to say that London is in England and Cairo in Egypt. On a good map we can find even much less important places, so long as we have an indication of the general area where they are located; for on earth we have given names to all the points anyone might wish to look for. Yet this is true only as long as we are looking for a place on dry land. The position of a ship at sea is given in a different way, by latitude and longitude. For this purpose, we draw on a globe from one pole to the other, at equal intervals, 360 semicircles which we call meridians of longitude; and, parallel to the equator, 180 full circles which we call parallels of latitude—90 between the equator and the North Pole, 90 between the equator and the South Pole. The ninetieth circle at each extreme is actually only a point—the pole.

The net of latitude and longitude circles may be seen on any globe. If the circles were a grid, and the rest of the earth transparent, we can imagine how a powerful light at the center of the earth would cast the shadow of these ribs on the celestial sphere.

This gives us the network we need for locating the stars. The terminology happens to be a little different. The two co-ordinates that mark a point in the heavens, as longitude and latitude mark a point on the earth, are called right ascension and declination. Declination is measured north and south of the equator (0° to +90, 0° to —90), and right ascension all the way round from 0° to 360°—or from 0 to 24 o'clock, because as a result of the earth's rotation the heavens seem to effect a complete revolution in 24 hours. The zero meridian, where the counting starts, must be established by agreement, as on earth, where it is the meridian of Greenwich. The zero meridian of the heavens passes through the point where the sun crosses the celestial equator in the spring, the vernal equinox. The system is very clear and simple. But to apply it in practice involves great difficulties.

How Astronomers Plot the Positions of the Stars

We leave the difficulties to the astronomers, and merely try to see how in general they go about establishing the position—the right ascension and declination—of a star. They use an instrument that looks very complicated, but whose workings are easy enough to understand if we strip it down to its essentials (Fig. 16).

FIG. 16. Diagram of a meridian circle.

We set up two posts along a line running from east to west. We cut notches in the tops and insert a stick which must be free to revolve. Through the middle of the stick we run a tube. We now have the essential part of a "meridian circle." As we turn the stick while looking through the tube or "telescope," our eye will pass across the sky in a half circle running from the south point on the horizon up to the zenith, and back down again to the north point. This half circle (the other half is concealed from us by the earth) is the meridian of our place of observation and serves as a line across which everything in the sky must move each day. When the sun passes the meridian, it is noon by real time, which differs slightly from standard time. The time from one such "transit" to the next is a 24-hour day, and we must set our clocks accordingly—for the real clock, from which everything takes its cue, is our earth, making one complete rotation each day and carrying us and our meridian around with it.

If we see a star pass across the field of our telescope today, we shall be able to catch it again tomorrow, provided we set the telescope at the same level above the horizon. Our star time clock must then show the same hour, minute, and second. If it doesn't, it is running fast or slow. Every star crosses the meridian at a definite hour and allows us to check our star time. The moment when a star crosses the meridian obviously depends on its position in the sky, specifically on its right ascension; every right ascension has a definite transit time. Conversely, a star that crosses the meridian at this moment can have only one definite right ascension. Thus, the meridian circle allows us to determine a star's right ascension.

A star's right ascension alone does not define its position in the sky, since there may be a large number of stars with the same right ascension. But we can attach to the axis a cogwheel with 360 teeth and measure how high (how many teeth or degrees) above the horizon the star crosses the meridian. We now have two coordinates which together can apply to only one star. Right ascension and declination (elevation above the celestial equator) give us the "position" of the star. Now we can find it and use it for astronomical purposes.

Of course, we are not going to get very far with our crude instrument. Astronomers reckon time and right

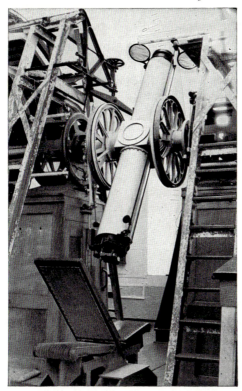

FIG. 17. Large meridian circle in the Hamburg Observatory.

ascension not in hours, or minutes, or even whole seconds, but in tenths, hundredths, and even thousandths of seconds. They do not measure declinations in whole degrees (which after all lie pretty close together), but in tenths and hundredths of a second of arc (one degree is divided into 60 minutes of arc, and one minute into 60 seconds of arc). This may give an idea why a real meridian circle is such a complicated apparatus (Fig. 17).

Catalogues and Charts for Millions of Stars

Astronomers first turned to the brightest stars and determined the positions of about 5000 of them that can be seen with the naked eye. But they did not stop here. By affixing powerful telescopes to their meridian circles they were able to observe fainter stars, and in the course of time the positions of several hundred thousand stars were established in this way. The star positions are entered in catalogues, of which the excerpt below is an example. Each line deals with a star. In addition to its number we find indications of its brightness in magnitudes, its right ascension and declination, and other figures with which we shall not concern ourselves. Astronomers also use star charts drawn according to the positions indicated in the catalogues. The most serviceable chart of this sort is the "Bonn Survey" (Bonner Durchmusterung), listed under column *BD* in the catalogue; for the stars of the southern sky that are not visible in Bonn we have a "Cordoba Survey" and a "Cape Town Photographic Survey."

NO.	BD		BR.	RIGHT ASC. 1925			DECL. 1925			EPOCH
1351	$+26°$	1690	9.3^m	7^h	54^m	9.44^s	$+26°$	$25'$	$23.6''$	1918.4
1352	$+16$	1598	6.0		54	14.89	$+16$	43	18.7	14.1
1353	$+10$	1677	8.3		54	41.57	$+10$	19	59.2	16.8
1354	$+51$	1381	8.5		54	51.76	$+50$	52	16.6	19.6
1355	$+52$	1268	8.9		55	6.48	$+51$	55	55.0	14.1

There are more stars in the sky than can be handled in this way. Astronomers deal with these masses of stars by photographs. A celestial photograph is actually a chart from which latitude and longitude lines are missing. We can draw them in if we know the right ascension and declination of a few of the stars in our photograph. But we can also do without this network, and make a few

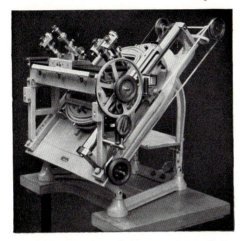

FIG. 18. Apparatus for measuring photographic plates (Hamburg Observatory).

measurements instead. We can, for instance, measure the distance of a star from the lower edge and the left edge of the plate. A few stars whose positions are known from a catalogue help us to determine what the measured fractions of an inch mean in the sky. We then can translate all our measurements into the usual indications. Such measurements, however, are not a simple matter. We must work in ten-thousandths or even hundred-thousandths of an inch, and such units cannot be read from an ordinary scale. The measuring apparatus we require is as different from a ruler as a real meridian circle is from the model we have built (Fig. 18). The *Photographic Star Chart* begun shortly before 1900 is an attempt to catalogue the great mass of faint stars. It comprises a large number of catalogues giving the positions of several million stars, and for many zones it provides charts that are direct reproductions of celestial photographs.

The *Palomar Sky Atlas* of the National Geographic

Society of the United States goes still further. The entire sky from the North Pole down to the part of the southern sky that can be seen from California is photographed with the big Schmidt telescope (Fig. 9), once without filter, once with a yellow filter. The whole collection of 2000 plates is reproduced photographically and placed at the disposal of observatories. These photographs show many more stars than the *Photographic Star Chart*, probably 500 million stars and 10 million remote star systems.

Astronomers Have Their Limitations

What are we going to do with these millions of star positions? It almost looks as though astronomers were just another foolish breed of collectors. But they have good reasons for their collecting. One of the reasons for determining so many star positions has nothing to do with the stars themselves. We need a dense network of fixed points in the sky as a means of following the courses of the planets and comets. The star catalogues still serve this purpose, but they also provide us with important information about the stars themselves.

Astronomers are not content to determine the position of a star only once. The desire to establish the position with as much precision as possible has led them to make repeated observations of the same star, sometimes in co-operation with other observatories. It would be too much to expect that they will obtain exactly the same result each time, for the observation of a star position is a complicated business. If the telescope is set at the proper elevation on the meridian, the star enters the telescope field of vision a little while before its transit. Several spider wires are installed (Fig. 19) at the focal plane of the object glass. The image of the star here moves from right to left, because the star out in space moves from left to right. We must now catch the moment at which the star passes across the vertical wire that marks our meridian. Even when this passage is clocked by means of an electrical signal that makes an automatic comparison with an astronomical clock, the same observer may in different instances arrive at slightly different results, and when more than one observer is involved, there is bound to be an even greater margin of error. A hundredth of a second is a mere instant, and even the best of observations are bound to show a variation of several such "instants." The same is true of the second part of our plotting. We must turn the telescope on its axis so that the star runs along the horizontal wire,

FIG. 19. Star in wire network (filar micrometer).

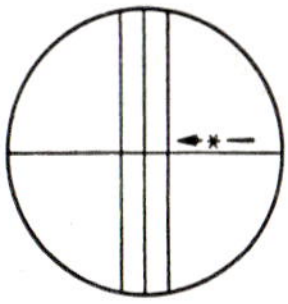

and then we must read the angle of our line of sight to the horizon on the circle that measures the rotation. The position is read with powerful microscopes, but even so a certain margin of error remains.

The observer himself is not the only source of imprecision. The instruments also contribute by flaws in their construction and changes caused by heat and cold, humidity, and other factors. The struggle against all these obstacles makes up a large part of the practical astronomer's activity. For what we have said of the meridian circle is equally true of all other astronomical instruments.

"Fixed" Stars Are Not Fixed

After we have used star catalogues for some time, we are able to judge how accurate the positions given in them are—how much larger and smaller the figures might be without implying a mistake or a change. When star positions are observed anew after a great deal of time—

after several decades, for example—the greater number of the stars show almost identical figures. But there are some stars whose position comes out quite different, and it will be different again if we observe them a third time, after another few decades. Of such stars we say that they have a motion of their own—a "proper motion" (Fig. 20). The following examples show how this is reflected in figures:

Star without proper motion	1890	19^h 40^m	54.05^s	−1°	46′	51.9″
	1908		54.04			52.3
	1919		54.02			51.9
Star with proper motion	1880	16^h 27^m	54.50^s	+3°	27′	52.1″
	1902		53.90			47.3
	1919		53.49			44.2

The supposedly "fixed" stars then do not keep their places in the heavens as unchangingly as we once thought. The changes of position are slight and do not catch the eye; long and complicated operations with star positions and star catalogues were needed before they could be noticed. But since we have been able to fix our view of the sky on photographic plates, such indirect methods are no longer necessary. We now can "see" the proper motions.

Let us take a look at the two photographs in Figure 21. Clearly, the arrangement of the stars in this part of the sky has in general remained unchanged. But if we look very closely at the center, we see that at least one of the two stars there has not stayed in place. This proper motion actually does "meet the eye," although it amounts

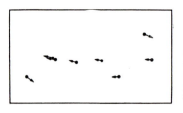

FIG. 20. The proper motions in 50,000 years of the best known stars in the Big Dipper. Six of the stars belong to a "star stream."

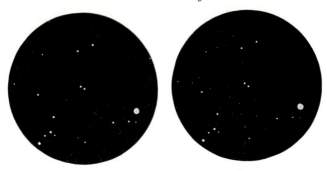

FIG. 21. A "fixed" star that has not stayed in place (photographs of the Heidelberg Observatory).

FIG. 22. A stereocomparator at the Hamburg Observatory.

to only 20 seconds of arc in the 14 years between the two exposures, and would take 1300 years to cover the breadth of the full moon.

To facilitate such comparisons, a special apparatus has been constructed, known as a stereocomparator (Fig. 22) because it serves to compare two plates. The two plates are set up side by side. Each of them is examined through a separate microscope. But the light rays are so guided that the rays from both microscopes enter the eye through the same opening. A movable shutter alternately covers one plate and then the other. If the plates are carefully paired, the general image will not change when the shutter shifts. But if a star in the field of vision has moved between the two exposures, it jumps back and forth as the shutter is shifted.

Most stars have very small proper motions, and if we wish to make them visible and measure them we must proceed with the utmost care. The simplest way would be to lay one plate on the other, so that nearly all the stars would coincide on the two plates, while the stars that have moved would make two dots side by side. We actually do proceed somewhat in this manner, but—as in all such cases—not exactly. Two plates cannot coincide perfectly, if only because we cannot produce two exactly identical photographs of the heavens at different times, even with the same telescope. It is more satisfactory to place the plates in such a way that the two pictures can be examined side by side, and the distance between them measured. This method requires computations that are sometimes very simple, at other times quite complex. But in the end it tells us how each star on the plates has moved in relation to the larger number of motionless stars.

The greatest proper motion thus far observed in a star is that of an inconspicuous faint star far below the visual threshold of the naked eye. Its proper motion is extraordinarily large (10 seconds of arc a year), but even so it would take almost 2000 years to pass along the outer edge of the Big Dipper. Proper motion thus would appear to be a very inconspicuous phenomenon. But it has far-reaching implications: it tells us that the world of the "fixed" stars is not static, and would not even seem to be so if we could observe it over a long period of time.

Small Proper Motions Mean Great Distances

The minuteness of the proper motions we observe does not mean that the motions of the stars are small. For what we see is merely the angle by which our line of sight moves in the course of time (Fig. 23), and this angle means a very different distance in space, according to the distance of the moving star. It may be that the stars are flying through space at great speeds, but are so far away that their motion seems small.

Let us assume for the moment that a star moves at the same speed as our earth does in its journey around the sun, roughly 20 miles a second. In a minute, it would travel 1200 miles, in an hour 72,000 miles, in a day ap-

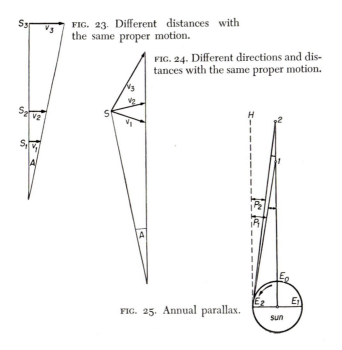

FIG. 23. Different distances with the same proper motion.

FIG. 24. Different directions and distances with the same proper motion.

FIG. 25. Annual parallax.

proximately 1.75 millions of miles, and in a year some 650 million miles. According to our observations, no star moves more than 10 seconds of arc in a year (the full moon has a diameter of 30 minutes or 1800 seconds of arc!). Thus its movement of 650 million miles appears to us as an angle of, at most, 10 seconds of arc. Now let us consider how far away this star must be if our figures are correct. If the angle a in Figure 23 amounted to only 10 seconds of arc (we cannot draw it so small), stretch v would be a mere point on the page. At a distance of one mile it would amount to 3 inches, at 1000 miles to 3000 inches, and at 1 million miles to 48 miles. In other words, the star must be at least 12 trillion miles away if its assumed motion of 20 miles a second is to fit in with the proper motion we have observed. But most of the stars have much smaller, almost imperceptible proper motions; hence we must reckon that they are a hundred or a thousand times farther away.

The Ten Largest Proper Motions

DESIGNATION OF STAR	BRIGHTNESS (IN MAGNITUDES)	PROPER MOTION (IN SECONDS OF ARC)
Barnard's star	9.5^m	10.3″
Kapteyn's star	9.2	8.7
Groombridge 1830	6.5	7.0
Lacaille 9352	7.2	6.9
Cordoba 32416	8.6	6.1
61 Cygni A and B	5.6; 6.3	5.2
Wolf 359	13.5	4.8
Lalande 21185	7.6	4.8
Epsilon Indi	4.7	4.7
Lalande 21258	8.5	4.5

The proper motions can thus give us two kinds of information about the stars—about their movements and their distances. But we should realize at once that they do not suffice for a complete knowledge of either. After measuring a star's proper motion, we can say something about its real motion only if we also know its distance. We must also bear in mind that we see and measure only what moves across our line of sight. The three motions drawn in Figure 24 differ greatly in extent and direction, but to us they represent the same angle. Hence, to determine fully the extent of a star's motion we need further information (see p. 134). But even a definite conclusion about the star's distance is beyond us. The distance can be computed from the proper motion only if we know the star's movement in space, and as a rule we do not.

The Distances of the Stars

We must admit that for the present there is little we can do with our precious proper motions. We first must find some method that will give us reliable knowledge of some other factor, such as the distance.

There are stars that astronomers observe not just every ten or twenty years but as often as possible. When we observe such a star in the spring and in the fall of this year, and again in the spring of next year, its position will by and large be the same, or else show a uniform change, a proper motion. But it may also be that the star changes its place slightly from spring to fall and in the next half year returns to its old position. This shuttling, in astronomy called parallax, is almost imperceptible, and parallax measurement is among the most difficult of the astronomer's tasks. But what does this shuttling mean? We might regard it as a peculiarity of the stars, if similarities in the back and forth of different stars did not lead us to seek the cause at our own doorstep.

We know that the spot from which we make our observations is exceedingly mobile. Day by day we are spun around as on a merry-go-round; in the course of a year, the whole merry-go-round itself circles round the sun. And it is from various points in this great circuit that we measure the positions of the stars. Let us look at Figure 25. Suppose that we sight our star at the very instant when the earth is exactly between the sun and the star (at E_0). We note its direction. Meanwhile the earth continues on its journey. When we arrive at E_2 we no longer see the star in the direction we had noted, E_2H (which is parallel to $E_0 1$). The line of sight has shifted by a very small angle. We measure the angle P_1 at E_2, which is the same as the other angles in our figure that are marked with double arrows. In other words, astronomers call "parallax" that angle at which the radius of the earth's orbit would appear from the star. The farther away the star, the smaller the angle. Thus, parallax is a measure of distance.

Surveying on Earth and in Space

Surveying the surface of the earth is something with which we are all familiar. Measuring the distance of a star is at bottom no different from what our surveyor

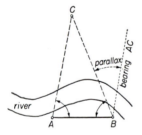

FIG. 26. Measurement of distance on earth.

does every day. If he wants to determine the position of point C (Fig. 26) without crossing the river, the surveyor establishes a base line AB and sights toward C from A and B. From the length of the base line AB, and the size of the two angles at A and B, the length of the lines AC and BC can be obtained by drawing or computation. This gives us the distance of point C. In our survey of outer space, the earth carries us automatically from one end of the base line to the other, and the only difficulty is to measure the angles, and to "retain" the original direction accurately enough to make the almost imperceptible change from one end of the base line to the other perceptible. This is not quite so simple as it might seem, and requires difficult observations and involved computations. Besides, only those stars that lie in the plane of the earth's orbit move simply back and forth—all others describe little ellipses.

There is one particular difficulty which we mention chiefly to show that it is really not easy for astronomers to penetrate the secrets of space. Let us return at point E_0 of the earth's orbit. Our telescope, we assume, is pointed in the direction of the light rays that come from the star; they pass through the object glass, and are gathered into an image at its focus. It will suffice to follow the ray that passes through the center of the object glass. By the time it arrives at the focus, the eyepiece of the telescope is no longer in position—it has meanwhile been carried along by the earth (*a* in Fig. 27). In order to see the star, we must be sure the eyepiece lags behind by this distance. We do it by slightly tilting the telescope (*b* in Fig. 27), though we thereby attribute a false position to the star.

Again, the phenomenon is not unfamiliar. We have all looked out of a train window in the rain. If a vertical rain begins to fall while the train is stopped, the raindrops drip straight down the windowpanes. But once the train is in motion, the drops move down the panes on a slant. If we hold a tube out the window, the drops that enter at the top will not come out again at the bottom as long as we hold the tube vertically. They will beat against the inner wall of the tube. But if we now tilt the tube toward the drops they will reach the lower end un-

FIG. 27. Aberration of light.   *a*   *b*

obstructed. The faster the train moves, the more obliquely we must hold our tube. The optical phenomenon,
the aberration of light, follows the same law.

The angle by which we must "advance" our telescope
is determined by the relation between the velocity of the
telescope (i.e., of the earth) and that of light (at point
E_0 30 : 300,000). It is not very large, but at 20 seconds
of arc it is still much larger than the largest parallax,
and we can imagine how difficult it is to prevent the
smaller phenomenon from being submerged by the larger.
That we can do it at all is due only to the fact that at
points E_1 and E_2, where the parallactic deviation is
greatest, there is no aberration, because here the telescope is moving in the direction of the light rays.

A Convenient Unit of Measurement: the Light-Year

We now no longer depend on vague estimates of star
distance such as those we arrived at with the help of the
stars' proper motions. The observation of parallaxes provides us with very definite figures, as tangible as any
earthly distance measured in the same way. Our estimates
had prepared us for great distances, but the real distances
prove to be far greater still. The largest parallax ever

measured amounts to only 0.8 seconds of arc, and the distance from which the 100-million-mile radius of the earth's orbit is seen at so small an angle—the angle at which a large coin would appear from a distance of 5 miles—comes to 25 trillion miles. The star that is so uncommonly close to us is a faint star in the constellation of Centaurus in the southern half of the sky. Sirius, the brightest star in the sky, is considerably farther: 56 trillion (56,000,000,000,000) miles.

No one will claim that he can visualize these distances, even if he has no difficulty in juggling the figures. It is simpler, and a little more acceptable to our imagination, to use a different yardstick. Miles are perfectly suitable for earthly distances—even the earth's circumference measures only some 25,000 miles. But they are not really suitable for cosmic space. Here we follow a custom common in daily life. Asked how far it is to the nearest mailbox, we do not usually say "three hundred yards" but, "three minutes." The time needed to travel a distance is used to express the distance itself. It does not always serve, because it is often not clear what means of travel we have in mind. But for outer space, only one means of communication need be considered—and that is light. A light signal sent out into space will one second later be seen 186,000 miles away. Shortly thereafter it will be on the moon. In a minute it will have traveled 11 million miles. In 8½ minutes it will have reached the sun. And if it was strong enough, it will go 6 trillion miles in a year's time. It has still not reached the nearest star, though it has traveled an appreciable part of the way. And so it makes good sense to use the distance that light travels in one year as a measure for cosmic distances. We call this distance a light-year. As we have just figured out it amounts to roughly 6 trillion miles. From now on we shall give all cosmic distances in light-years.

The Brightest Stars Are Not the Nearest

We now draw up two lists of the most important stars whose distances we know through measurements of their parallaxes. One list contains the nearest stars, the other the brightest ones—with which we are most familiar. The distances shown in parentheses have not been computed by parallax but by other methods which we shall discuss later.

The Nearest Stars

We note at once that the brightest stars are not the closest. This is important to keep in mind, for, if all

NAME	BRIGHTNESS (IN MAGNITUDES)	DISTANCE (IN LIGHT-YEARS)
Proxima Centauri	11.0	4
Alpha Centauri	0.1	4
Barnard's star	9.7	6
Wolf 359	13.5	8
Luyten 726–8	12.5	8
Lalande 21185	7.6	8
Sirius	−1.6	9

The "First Magnitude" Stars

NAME	DISTANCE (IN LIGHT-YEARS)	NAME	DISTANCE (IN LIGHT-YEARS)
Sirius	9	Altair	16
Canopus	(650)	Betelgeuse	(270)
Alpha Centauri	4	Alpha Crucis	(220)
Vega	27	Aldebaran	57
Capella	48	Pollux	30
Arcturus	38	Spica	(300)
Rigel	(540)	Antares	(160)
Procyon	11	Fomalhaut	27
Achernar	72	Deneb	very great
Beta Centauri	91	Regulus	80

stars were equally bright, those which appear brightest would be nearest. The fact that they are not tells us that stars can vary greatly in luminosity. A star that seems very bright may have a relatively small luminosity and be very close to us (Sirius), or it can have great luminosity and be very far away (Canopus). It would be much more convenient if all stars had the same luminosity—then their apparent brightness would tell us clearly how far away they are. We would know where all visible stars are situated in space and would almost have a model of the stellar world. But as things are, we must obtain our information by intricate indirect methods.

Natural Limits

For the time being we must be content to know something about our immediate vicinity—only our most immediate vicinity, for the longest distances we can establish at all accurately with our surveyors' methods go up to some 150 light-years, and that is not very much. But we might as well face the fact that we shall extend this limit only very slightly and very slowly. Distance, we remember, is measured by the angle between the star's two positions as seen from opposite ends of the earth's orbit. The more distant the star, the smaller this angle, and it finally becomes so small that the errors which creep into our measurements are as large as the angle itself.

To illustrate, let us assume that a star is 3.25 light-years distant. The angle we have to measure in this case amounts to one second of arc. We cannot measure it with absolute precision. Our measurements may yield 1.1 or 0.9 seconds of arc, a deviation of 10 per cent either way. The distance we derive from our measurement may, therefore, be 10 per cent off. We may arrive at 2.9 or 3.5 light-years instead of the correct 3.25. This is not a great error, and for most purposes our result will suffice. But matters are different if we want to measure a distance of 32 light-years. Now the parallax will amount to only 0.1 second of arc, and since our errors of observation may again produce a deviation of 0.1 second of arc either way, our measurement may come to either 0.0 or 0.2 seconds of arc. But a parallax of 0.2 second of arc corresponds to a distance of 16 light-years (instead of 32), whereas a parallax of 0.0 means an infinite distance. Clearly, the inaccuracy of our observations sets a limit beyond which we cannot pass, try as we may. We can today measure parallaxes more accurately than in the above example, but we cannot vouch for distances beyond 150 light-years. The accuracy of our observations will gradually improve with our instruments and methods, but not so much as to extend appreciably the field of the sky accessible to direct measurement.

There is still another way to measure distances more accurately, and to measure greater distances: we choose a longer base. If we could move to one of the outer planets which revolve around the sun in much larger orbits, we should have a base from 5 times (on Jupiter) to 30 times (on Neptune) as large as our base on the earth. But for the present we cannot count on such excursions. The earth's orbit with its diameter of 187 million miles represents a natural limit.

Looking out of the Train Window

We compared our journey round the sun to a ride on a merry-go-round. The comparison is apt. But a ride on a merry-go-round, going in a circle, is not the clearest and simplest way of seeing parallaxes. We shall do better by sitting down in a railway car. Look out the window: the landscape moves like a revolving stage. The part close to the tracks flies past; more distant objects move slowly, and the far background almost stands still.

Figures 28 and 29 show the reason. In Figure 28 points

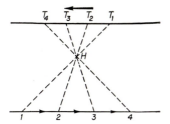

FIG. 28. Progressive parallax.

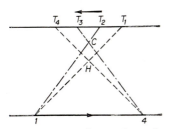

FIG. 29. Dependence of parallactic shift on distance.

1, 2, 3, 4 mark spots along the line of our journey. H is a house in an open field, at some distance from the tracks. In the background there is a highway, lined with trees. As we travel from 1 to 4, we see the house moving in the opposite direction from one tree on the highway to another, from T_1 to T_2, T_3 and T_4. In the triangle with the corners 1, 4, and H, the angle at H is the parallax of point H in relation to the base 1–4, and we see from the figure that we can determine this angle and the distance of the house H from the track by measuring the distance 1–4, and the two angles at 1 and 4, between the railway line and the directions in which we see the house from the two points. Once we know the length of the line 1–4, we can draw it to scale; at 1 and 4 we draw the angles we have measured: then the two legs of the triangle thus formed will intersect at H.

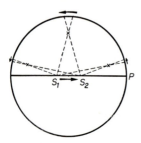

FIG. 30. Parallactic movements in the sky brought about by the motion of the sun.

In Figure 29 only two points of our stretch of railway are drawn, but in addition to the house there is a church C, which is farther away. The church also appears to move along the background from tree to tree, but only from the second to the third, while the house moves from the first to the fourth: the smaller apparent motion corresponds to the greater distance. This is exactly what we experienced in measuring the distance of a star. Still, our railway journey tells us something new: the farther we continue our journey, the greater becomes the parallactic shift for the same object. If we take time enough, there is a chance that the shifts of very distant objects may become large enough for us to observe.

We Find Similar Phenomena in the Sky

What good does this knowledge do us? It can be put to use only if we travel through the sky steadily and swiftly, and so far we are not aware of any such motion. Yet this is what actually happens. The earth moves round the sun, and so do the other planets, but the whole solar system itself is moving too. For countless years it has been traveling through space at a speed of roughly 12 miles a second. Even within the short time span of our experience it covers considerable distances: 45,000 miles an hour; 375 million miles a year. This motion enables us to observe those increasing parallactic shifts of the stars that we have illustrated in our example. And now let us see how this looks in the sky.

Our motion proceeds in a straight line, but the background against which we see and estimate the parallactic shifts behaves somewhat differently from the highway in our example. The sky looks round to us, and for our present purposes it is legitimate to regard it as a great hollow ball. Figure 30 illustrates what takes place. It shows three stars (x, x, x) all at the same distance from us. But they differ in their position relative to the point P toward which our motion is tending. One is "ahead of us," the second "off to one side," the third "behind us." As the sun carries us from S_1 to S_2, all three undergo an apparent shift in the same direction: away from P. The shift is greatest for the star off to the side, and very small for the two others, ahead and behind.

The three diagrams in Figure 31 show how the parallactic shifts of the stars are grouped in the vicinity of the three points in question. If our velocity were greater, it would look as though the stars ahead of us were moving to one side to get out of our way, passing us by very quickly, and then closing in again behind us. Only a star that was exactly in our path would not move aside. We gain the same impression when we drive through

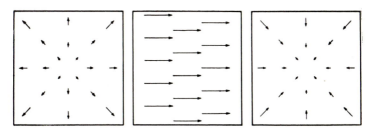

FIG. 31. Schematic drawing of how the stars seem to move as we journey through them with the sun: ahead of us (left), behind us (right), and in the intervening zone (middle).

the woods. Ahead of us the trees move slowly aside, at the right and left of us they pass by swiftly, and behind us they close in again, to become once more a motionless forest. A tree standing in the middle of the road would not reflect our motion in this way. But there is another way in which we can observe that we are coming closer, and we shall later find that it is possible to read our motion from the stars in a similar fashion (see p. 134).

We have taken the motion of our solar system through starry space for granted, and then have shown how it must be reflected in the sky. Actually, our knowledge was gathered in the opposite order. Astronomers discovered the motion of the sun after observing the parallactic shifts of the stars; they derived the direction and velocity of the motion from the distribution and magnitude of the parallactic changes. This was not as simple as we make it appear. The parallactic shifts appear to us as proper motions of the stars, and we have seen how proper motions are found by repeated observation of star positions. Such slight motions are hard to disentangle from errors of observation, although this is no longer so troublesome since we can wait until the shifts have become large enough. A much more serious difficulty is created by the stars themselves.

If the stars stood still in their places in outer space, the parallactic shifts would appear clearly and plainly. But they are no more at rest than is our sun. Just like the sun, each star moves at its own velocity in its own direction, so that we are up against an intricate muddle of proper motions which we must sort out in order to compute the parallactic shifts. With patience and ingenuity this can be done, provided we assume that the movements of the stars follow no law, that there is no "system" in them. We take a patch of sky as large as the Big Dipper or Orion, and group together the proper motions of a few dozen stars to find a mean value. What is irregular—that is, different from star to star—is canceled out in such a process; what is common to all the stars in our group, their parallactic shift, is expressed by our mean figure.

But how has all this helped us to improve our determination of distances? In this way: large parallaxes mean small distances, and small parallaxes mean large distances; once we determine the motion of our sun, we can compute those distances. Hence we have achieved what we set out to do: the longer we continue our observations, the longer our base grows and the greater are the distances we can measure. But this method gives us no help in determining the distance of a single star. Since we must work with a large number of stars in order to cancel out the proper motion of each of them, we obtain the distance only for the whole group, and this is useful only if that group consists largely of stars at the same distance from the earth. Here we have a *statistical* method; such methods are extremely important, but demand a great deal of knowledge and ingenuity if they are to yield insights rather than errors.

Double Stars

What proper motions tell us about the real movements of the stars will become wholly clear only later on, in connection with other observations. For the moment, we note that after the periodic and progressive parallactic shifts (and of course the aberration) have been counted out from the proper motions we observe, there remain real cross motions of the stars which are in general rectilinear and uniform.

The result is different only when two stars are close together. The observation of bright double stars—binaries—was begun more than a hundred years ago, and present catalogues contain more than 20,000 such binary systems. We establish the position of the two stars relative to one another by measuring, first the "distance" between them, next the angle formed by a line joining them and another line drawn toward the north celestial pole. (On the focal plane of a telescope, or on a photographic plate, the distance between the images of stars may be measured in inches; but transferred to the sky, it signifies an angle between two directions and is expressed in seconds of arc.)

The great majority of double stars show the same position over and over again, in observation after observation. This occurs even with stars that are not very close together, as well as with whole groups of stars, and may mean that the stars are moving side by side at the same speed. But in the case of the fainter binaries it usually means that both stars are too far away, from us and from one another, for their relative motion to show. Then, their motion relative to one another is so slow that we can hope to recognize it only after hundreds of years. But in other cases it is worthwhile to note the positions established at different times. Figure 32 gives us such a picture for the double star Gamma Virginis. In the hundred years covered by our observations one of the two stars has completed more than half an ellipse around

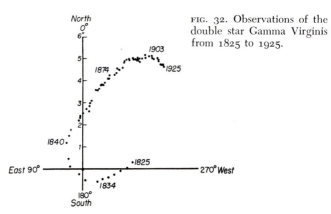

FIG. 32. Observations of the double star Gamma Virginis from 1825 to 1925.

the other. A more complete circuit has been observed only in rare cases; but the partial circuit allows us to determine the shape of the orbit and the length of the period, since we know that two masses can move around one another only in either circles or ellipses. We must bear in mind that in most cases our line of sight is not perpendicular to the orbit, that we do not see the orbit in its true form. We can, however, rectify the image and derive the shape, position, and magnitude (in angles) of the true orbit. Today we have adequate determinations of the orbits of 250 binary systems; the periods range from a few years to several centuries.

Comparing the Stars with Our Sun

Once we have determined the distance of a double star of this type, we can compute the diameter of its orbit in miles. This is extremely important, because one of the laws of mechanics permits us to compute the total mass of the double star (in comparison with the mass of the sun) from the length of its period and the diameter of its orbit, and there is no other way to arrive at the mass of stars. Of course, we still do not know how the total mass is distributed between the two stars, that is, how much matter each of them contains; but in certain cases even this can be computed.

In Gamma Virginis in Figure 32, both stars are bright: hence it makes no difference which one we assume to be at rest. Where the two stars of a binary system differ in brightness, the brighter one is usually considered the stationary main star against which the position of the fainter companion star is measured. But if we measure the other way around—if we assume the fainter star to be at rest and measure the position of the brighter one in relation to it—our result is just as correct.

We can replace these relative orbits by absolute ones if—by means of a meridian circle or a photographic plate

—we can determine the positions of the two stars in conjunction with the positions of stars that are really at rest. We then can establish a reference point between the two stars (the center of gravity of the system) and find for each of the two stars an orbit around this center, which may be regarded as stationary, or as moving evenly with other stars. The two orbits may differ in size; if so, the difference expresses the ratio between their masses. From this ratio and their total mass, we can compute their individual masses.

Furthermore, in observing a single star we may find changes of position that reveal an elliptical motion and hence the presence of an invisible companion star. The fainter companions of the bright stars Sirius and Procyon were looked for on the basis of such calculations—and ultimately found. The motions of some binary systems are not purely elliptical; we may then assume the presence of a third or even a fourth star, and sometimes we can even compute their positions.

Masses of a Few Double Stars

STAR	PERIOD (IN YEARS)	MASSES OF THE TWO STARS	
Capella	0.3	4.0 × sun	3.6 × sun
Sirius	50	2.2	1.0
Procyon	40	1.4	0.4
Xi Boötis	151	0.5	0.5
Krüger 60	44	0.3	0.2
85 Pegasi	26	0.5	0.4
61 Cygni	720	0.6	0.6

II. BRIGHTNESS

Differences in Brightness

The stars are not all equally bright. How are we to compare their brightness? As a rule it is not difficult to say which one of two stars is the brighter, but it is hardly possible to say that one star is two or three times as bright as the other. It is easier to find a third star that in brightness is between the two. We can go and insert another star between the first and second, and between the second and third, and so arrive at a whole scale of brightness. After working long enough with such a scale, an observer will have it imprinted so strongly on his mind that even when looking at two stars that do not differ greatly he can estimate how many degrees of brightness separate them. This method is natural, and is still used in many cases.

But it has one flaw: degree of brightness is no objective measure, its meaning varies slightly for each observer. We need to find a standard. To this end we shall sacrifice half a dozen photographic plates, exposing them for a short time and then developing them. They are now slightly blackened, and as we look through them everything looks a little darker. The plates swallow up a fraction of the light that shines on them, and if they are all equally black, they will all absorb the same fraction of light. With this equipment we make an experiment on the sky.

We observe two stars, one of them clearly brighter than the other. We take one of our plates and look through it at both stars. The difference in brightness does not change; they both grow fainter. But if we look only at the brighter one through the plate, at the other with the naked eye, the difference in brightness grows less. If the brighter star still looks brighter, we look at it through two of our plates. Now the brighter star looks exactly as bright as the fainter one—and we may say that it is two degrees brighter. And if we hand our plates to another observer, he will come to the same conclusion, for he is using the same "standard." With our plates we may compare as many stars as we like. Wherever two plates make the brightness equal, we have the same difference in brightness. We are now entitled to speak of *differences* in brightness: the plate becomes a unit of measurement.

But consider exactly what happens in this method of observation. Suppose we are dealing with a number of stars. We make the faintest one our norm. Let us say that the next brighter one is as faint as the norm if looked at through one plate; while the third is as faint as the norm when its light passes through two plates. Let us suppose that our plates are so blackened that they swallow one-half of the light. The quantity of light that passes through is consequently only half the original light quantity i; what gets through the second plate is then only a half of a half, or $\frac{1}{4} i$; what passes through three plates is $\frac{1}{2}$ of $\frac{1}{4} i$ or $\frac{1}{8} i$, and so on. If, after this reduction of their light, respectively, through no plate, one plate, two plates, three plates, and so on, the stars of our series all look equally bright, then the original quantity of light emitted by the second star must be twice as large as that of the first; the light of the third, 4 times as great; of the fourth, 8 times; and so on:

Star	1	2	3	4	5	6
Original quantity of light	1	2	4	8	16	32
Number of plates	0	1	2	3	4	5
Remaining light	1	1	1	1	1	1

This calculation shows that equal degrees in our observation correspond, not to equal differences, but to equal proportions in light quantity. In our example, using plates so blackened that they absorbed one-half of the light, each interval signifies a relation of 2 : 1. If we had selected plates that absorbed only 10 per cent of the light, our table would show different figures, but our method of reckoning would be the same.

Star "Magnitudes"

Our eye works on the same principle. All observations concerning difference in brightness must, therefore, be translated into relations between quantities of light. For almost two thousand years, we have had a classification of the stars according to their brightness estimated by eyesight. It divides the stars visible to the naked eye into six classes. The brightest stars form the first, the faintest the sixth magnitude class. In keeping with old custom we speak of stars of the first, second, third, fourth, fifth, or sixth "magnitude," but we mean their brightness, not their spatial magnitude.

These old magnitude classes still provide the framework of our classification. We at last began to measure the brightness of the stars with the help of photometers (instruments for measuring light) and to reckon according to a fixed scale, the scale so divided that it would match the classes of the historical scale. It turned out that the difference in brightness from one magnitude to the next meant a ratio of intensity of 2.5 : 1—in other words, a star of the first magnitude gives us 2.5 times as much light as a star of the second. It follows that we obtain $2.5 \times 2.5 = 6.25$. times as much light from a star of the first magnitude as from a star of the third. If we continue we find that for a difference of 5 magnitudes the light of the brighter star is approximately 100 times as strong as that of the fainter one; 10 magnitudes mean a relation of 10,000 : 1. To provide a familiar reference for comparison we note that a hundred-watt bulb held 6.25 miles away would look to us like a star of the first magnitude.

We designate brightness no longer by magnitude, but by a number, just as we read temperature in numbers on the thermometer. There are stars of magnitudes 1.0, 2.0, 3.0, 4.0, 5.0, and 6.0. Between them lie stars of magnitudes 1.5, 2.5, . . ., and there are also stars of magnitudes 1.1,

1.2, 1.3, etc. In highly accurate measurements we even use the hundredth part of a magnitude, arriving at figures such as 1.73 or 5.69.

There is no longer any reason why we should stop at the sixth magnitude. Our scale can continue as far as we like—in fact we are compelled to extend it, because the great majority of stars are much fainter. The largest telescopes today take us below the twentieth magnitude, and this is only a temporary limit of our scale. Nor is 1.0 the limit at the other end, since there are some stars that are brighter. Their gradations are again given just as on a thermometer: 1.0, 0.9, 0.8 . . . 0.1, 0.0, —0.1, —0.2, and so on. (A star of magnitude —1.0 is 2 magnitudes brighter than a star of magnitude 1.0.) We need not carry the scale very far in this direction, for the brightest of stars, Sirius, has a magnitude of —1.6. But if later on we should run into magnitudes such as —5 or —10, we shall know how they fit into our scale. The magnitude of the full moon is —12, of the sun —27. The brightness of the best known stars is shown in the table on page 76.

Measuring Brightness with a Telescope

We have insisted that our scale of brightness must be based on exact measurements. How are such measurements made? Our photographic plate method is neither convenient nor always practicable. If two stars are close together it is easy to tell whether they are of the same brightness, because we can easily move our eye to the second before we have forgotten our impression of the first; but if we wish to compare two stars at opposite ends of the sky, we have difficulty. Above all, our method must be suitable for telescopic observation, since most of the stars can be seen only through a telescope. We must build our gradations, or something corresponding to them, into the telescope.

Figure 33 shows how this is done. The object glass of

the telescope gathers the light of the star we are observing into a luminous point on its focal plane. We attach a short elbow at the side of the telescope and fasten a small light bulb in its end. A lens in the elbow produces an image of the bulb. In order to get this image in the focal plane of the telescope's object glass, we insert into the telescope an oblique glass plate which casts the rays from the light bulb in the proper direction. (It need not trouble us that part of the artificial light passes through the plate, while a part of the light from the star does not pass through it but is thrown to one side.) Through the eyepiece of the telescope, we see two stars side by side —the natural and the artificial star, grouped conveniently—as we shall not easily find in the sky. To compare the two seems at first to serve no purpose. But when we have compared a second and a third star with our artificial one, we know the relation of brightness between the three natural stars, and this is what we intended. The artificial star merely forms a bridge from one star to another, and makes us independent of our memory, which is not very reliable in this respect.

Next, we attempt to build our fixed gradations into the telescope so that we may not have to rely on our subjective estimates. There is a very simple device, also very

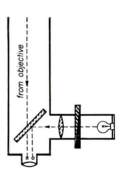

FIG. 33. Diagram of telescope with photometer.

easy to handle: the dark wedge. Figure 33 shows within the elbow a glass plate composed of two wedge-shaped parts, one transparent, the other opaque. This dark plate (known as a wedge, because for light measurement it is only the opaque wedge that matters) can be moved (in the figure, up and down). According to the position of the wedge, which can be read on a scale, the light coming from the bulb must travel a greater or lesser distance through the dark glass and is correspondingly fainter or brighter when it arrives at the focal plane of the telescope. In measuring the light of the star, we move the wedge until the natural star and the artificial star, which at first differ in brightness, appear equally bright. We do so with every star whose brightness we wish to measure, and in each case note the reading on the scale. The differences in the position of the wedge give us the differences in the brightness of the stars. To translate these differences into the customary magnitudes, we must, of course, determine the relation of our scale to the magnitudes. This is a very important task, which can be accomplished by measuring stars whose differences in brightness are already known, or by measuring in the laboratory a light source whose brightness we can change in some accurately measurable way (such as by varying the current passing through a bulb, or by modifying the opening through which the light must pass).

Eyes That See Better than Natural Eyes

The wedge photometer is not the only instrument used for measuring light, but it is the instrument best suited to showing us the nature of such measurements. The various types of photometer are designed to create the most favorable conditions for observation; it is the human eye, however, that must finally decide. Our eye is a remarkably efficient organ, but it was made for the needs of daily life, not for astronomical measurements. Hence

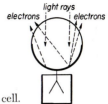

FIG. 34. The principle of a photoelectric cell.

we must not be surprised to find that the eye does not differentiate brightness as accurately as we need for certain problems.

For measurements of great precision, the natural eye is replaced by an artificial one, a "photoelectric cell" (Fig. 34). This is a glass ball, a "glass eye," the "retina" of which consists of a very thin layer of metal (the substances that may be used are potassium, sodium, cesium, lithium, and rubidium). This layer of metal is connected with an electrometer. As long as the cell is in the dark, nothing happens, the little leaves of the electrometer hang limp. But as soon as light from the telescope falls on the "retina," particles of electricity (electrons) flow from it. Since only negative electricity flows off, an excess of positive electricity remains, and the leaves of the electrometer spread open, because they both have a positive charge and repel one another. The amount of electricity that flows off corresponds exactly to the intensity of the light that falls. Measuring the differences in brightness with the electrometer yield results ten times as precise as those obtained with other photometers.

When these photoelectric cells—which are employed also for sound film and television—are built into a telescope, other elaborate apparatus must be added. High tension apparatus or a set of high tension batteries is needed to accelerate the motion of the liberated electrons sufficiently to produce a current; we also need boosters, and finally the actual measuring instruments, some of which record their readings automatically. This photo-electric equipment is in growing use.

Photographic Measurement of Brightness

The brightness of stars can also be determined from sky photographs. It is a basic principle of photography that bright objects will appear blacker on a photographic plate than dark ones. A bright star will form a blacker spot on a plate than a fainter one. But there is still another difference: the brighter star will make a *larger* spot. This is not self-evident, and actually it seems a little strange. To the telescope objective, the stars are all immensely distant points, and the cones of light emanating from them strike the plate in little circles, which are not so very much larger for bright stars than for faint ones. It is only in the photographic plate itself that the image increases in diameter when the light is brighter or the exposure is longer. The result is that a photograph of the sky looks like a star chart on which the stars have been drawn in varying sizes according to their brightness.

Thanks to this phenomenon, we can measure the brightness of the stars by measuring the diameters of their images. This is a linear measurement and hence very convenient. We achieve greater precision, however, by measuring the blackening of the plates, that is, the thickness of the silver precipitation. This is a process similar to the measurement of the brightness of stars in the sky and is carried out with similar apparatus.

Different Kinds of Brightness

We have, then, a considerable choice of instruments with which to determine the brightness of stars. One would think that in each case we need only choose the most accurate and convenient method. But when we set to work with this idea, we soon meet some very curious surprises. Of what kind they are is illustrated by the two pictures in Figure 35, one of which (left) shows the constellation of Orion as it appears to the eye (what we call "visual" magnitude), the other (right) as it appears on an ordinary (not panchromatic) photographic plate. The difference between the two pictures is striking. The star at the upper left (Alpha Orionis, Betelgeuse) is considerably brighter to the eye than the one at the upper right (Gamma Orionis); it is almost as bright as Beta (Rigel) at the lower right. On the "photograph," however, Alpha is by far the faintest of the three.

STAR	VISUAL MAGNITUDE	PHOTOGRAPHIC MAGNITUDE
Alpha Orionis	0.9	2.3
Beta Orionis	0.3	0.3
Gamma Orionis	1.7	1.5

What we have found here is no peculiarity of these stars, but occurs whenever we measure brightness both visually and photographically: the two methods do not yield the same result. Obviously, the plate *sees differently* from the eye; but different in what respect? Every photographer knows that the colors of objects are transmitted differently by a plate and by the eye. Blue or violet objects come out too light in the print, too black in the negative, yellow or red objects come out too dark in the print. The eye is most sensitive to yellow light—the photographic plate reacts most strongly to blue and violet light. Since we want pictures that show things as we see them, we take our photographs today with plates and film which have been specially sensitized to yellow and red light. We use such emulsions also for celestial photographs—for example, those made to determine visual brightness. When we speak of "photographic brightness," we mean brightness according to ordinary plates sensitive to blue and violet.

FIG. 35. The constellation Orion photographed (left) with panchromatic film and (right) with film not sensitive to red. These photographs were made with an ordinary 35 mm. camera.

Is the Light of the Stars Colored?

Two stars, then, that seem equally bright to the eye may differ in brightness on a photographic plate—if they differ in color. A superficial observer of the sky will call this absurd—he remembers all stars as "white." But let him take a little more time and compare carefully the stars that happen to be visible at the moment.

If Orion happens to be in the sky (in the winter), the stars in Figure 35 may serve as an example. Compare Alpha and Beta Orionis. Anyone who is not color blind will see at once that Beta is really white, Alpha is red—though not quite as red as a traffic light. To the lower left of Orion, Sirius (in Canis Major) is white; Aldebaran to the upper right (in Taurus) is reddish. In the summer sky Vega (in Lyra), Deneb (in Cygnus), and Altair (in Aquila)—the stars of the distended triangle—are more or less white; Arcturus (in Boötes) and Antares (in Scorpio) are red or at least yellow. And if anyone should come along and maintain that our white stars are blue, our yellow stars white, and our deep red ones faint yellow, we could only tell him that he sees more accurately than the rest of us. If the stars were large surfaces (like the moon or even Jupiter, Saturn, and Mars in the telescope), we should see all their colors as he does; but in judging faint points, our color scale shifts toward red.

What Is "Brightness"?

It follows from all we have said that we cannot simply speak of the "brightness" of the stars. Every star sends out radiation of a definite intensity, which we could call its brightness if only we could measure it. But we cannot. The radiation must undergo all sorts of vicissitudes before we can capture and measure it. Its long journey from the star to the earth is relatively untroubled; but then it must pass through the earth's atmosphere and through the lenses of the telescope and of the eye, before being finally registered on a photographic plate, on the metal coating of a photoelectric cell, or on our retina. At each turn, some of the radiation is absorbed. And although we do not always compute the intensity of the radiation before it entered the earth's atmosphere, we must at least indicate all brightnesses as they would be measured under standard conditions generally agreed upon. Accordingly, we always indicate zenith brightness—that is, the brightness a star would have if it stood directly over the observer, so that its light passed vertically through the earth's atmosphere, thus incurring the least loss.

More disturbing than the absorption of light is the fact that this absorption is not uniform for all colors. Different-colored stars that seem equally bright at the zenith become unequal as they approach the horizon. All stars lose more of their photographic brightness than of their visual brightness as they approach the horizon, because they become redder. These differences, which for observations close to the horizon amount to several magnitudes, must be determined by experiment and computation, and taken into account when the observations are translated into "normal" terms. But even after our observations have been translated into terms of zenith brightness, discrepancies still remain. We arrive at different brightnesses according to the different methods by which we capture and measure the radiation. For each receiver (eye, plate, photoelectric cell) uses only a part of the radiation falling upon it, as is shown in the sensitivity curves in Figure 36. This gives rise to a rather complex state of affairs. We shall try to form a general idea of it.

Assume we are comparing two stars of identical color. The radiation of these stars is composed of all possible colors, but the distribution of the different colors is the same in both stars, for otherwise their over-all color could not be the same. Now if one of the two stars is three times as bright as the other, the part of the radiation falling to each color is also three times as great, and so is the part that the eye uses—both for each color and for the whole. The same holds true for a photographic plate. It, too, indicates three times as much radiation, since the brighter star provides it with three times as much light

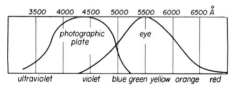

FIG. 36. Sensitivity curves for the eye and for the red-insensitive plate. The elevation of the curve above the base line indicates the sensitivity. Wave lengths are given in Ångstrom units (1Å = 0.0000001 millimeter).

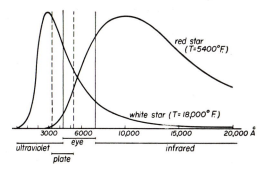

FIG. 37. Radiation relation between a white and a
red star that seem equally bright to the eye.

in each color. Thus in each case we measure correct
brightness, and if we wish we can designate them by the
same system, so that a star of visual brightness 8.0 will
also have photographic brightness 8.0, a star of visual
brightness 10.0 will have photographic brightness 10.0,
and so on. If we have been dealing only with white stars,
we are even in agreement with the conventions of the
astronomers. But if along with the white star of brightness
8.0 we have a red star which the eye declares to be
equally bright, it does not look as large and black on the
plate as does its white neighbor, but appears considerably fainter, almost as faint as a white star of the tenth
magnitude.

The reason is shown in Figure 37. On the base line,
colors are given in a numerical order whose significance
we shall learn later. The elevation of the curve over the
base line shows that radiation in each of the two stars
is distributed among the various colors. We see at once
that the white star radiates most strongly in ultraviolet,
the red star in infrared. The total radiation can also be
taken from the figure: it is represented by the area enclosed between the curve and the base line. The part of
the radiation that is utilized by the eye (or by the plate)

is the part of the surface that is between the two solid (or dotted) vertical lines enclosing the corresponding color zones. In our example the surfaces affecting the eye are equally great for both curves; to the eye, therefore, both stars are equally bright. But to the photographic plate (between the dotted lines), the white star provides a much larger surface than the red one, because its intensity curve is here very high, while that of the red star approaches the base line (or zero). The plate takes 4 times as much radiation from the white star as from the red one. Translating intensity relations into brightness means that the red star is photographically $1\frac{1}{2}$ magnitudes fainter than the white star.

This explains why our photographic brightnesses must differ from the visual ones. We can make similar computations for photoelectric brightnesses. But as we study Figure 37, a very different question arises. Why do we not measure the *total* radiation, which is so very large in the red star? As a matter of fact, this could be done, but it is much more difficult, and the method used has only of late been applied to the stars. It is based on the knowledge that whenever radiation is absorbed—whether or not it is perceptible to the eye or the photographic plate—it is transformed into heat. The method is based on devising a mechanism that will absorb a maximum of radiation and will then indicate in some way how much heat has been produced. In a manner of speaking, we shall be taking the stars' temperature with a thermometer. This may sound a little strange, but it is exactly what we have in mind.

Measuring the Temperature of the Stars

Now let us see how far we shall get with a common mercury thermometer. What does such an instrument do? If we apply heat to the mercury in the ball of the thermometer, it requires more room than before. More mercury must pass from the ball into the tube of the thermometer, and the thin column of mercury whose end indicates the temperature becomes longer. Ordinarily, the heat passes to the mercury directly by "conduction" from the matter surrounding the ball of the thermometer—from the air, or from the water in which we immerse the thermometer. But heat can enter the mercury also in the form of radiation—to wit, a thermometer on which the sun shines shows higher temperature than a thermometer protected from direct radiation (temperature "in the sun" and "in the shade"). We can greatly increase the effect of the radiation by coating the normally shiny ball of the thermometer with soot, so that it reflects as little and absorbs as much of the radiation as possible. We can even arrange to measure only the effect of the radiation, and cut off the conduction of heat between the mercury and the surrounding air, by setting the whole thermometer in an airtight glass tube from which all air has been pumped (the principle of the thermos bottle).

Such and similar thermometers are used for measuring the sun's radiation. There seems to be no reason why they should not be used to measure stellar radiation. Since the radiation we receive from the stars is much fainter than that of the sun we must, of course, refine our methods. We shall not simply let the light of a star fall on the soot-coated thermometer ball, but use a telescope, setting the thermometer ball in the focus of the object glass or reflector. This will allow us to take advantage of the much greater quantity of radiation that is gathered in by the large aperture of the telescope. We also select a thermometer with a very small mercury ball, because a given amount of heat will, of course, warm a small quantity of mercury more than it will a large one. We can go on working out still other refinements—but in spite of it all we shall not be able to demonstrate the

FIG. 38 and FIG. 39. Diagram of a thermoelement.

radiation of a star with a mercury thermometer. The direct radiation of the sun, without amplification, can make the thread of mercury rise 80° F. above room temperature; but even with the help of the great Mt. Palomar reflector, the brightest star will not raise the mercury in our thermometer by one thousandth of a degree. To measure such minute quantities of heat we must devise a different apparatus delicate enough for our purposes. There are several such instruments (bolometers, radiometers); let us examine only one of them, the thermoelement, which has been used very successfully with stars.

The thermoelement is an electrical thermometer. It consists of two wire filaments of different metals (such as iron and copper) whose ends are twisted or soldered together (Fig. 38). When we heat one of the joints between such wires (A in the illustration), an electric current runs through the circuit. If we heat the other joint B, the current flows in the opposite direction. The currents produced in this way are not dangerous; even with the best choice of metals (antimony and bismuth), an increase in temperature of 180° will create a tension of only $\frac{1}{100}$ volt, whereas a flashlight battery has a tension of two to six volts. But, fortunately, such feeble currents can be measured with great precision.

To connect a galvanometer to measure the current (Fig. 39), we cut one of the wires and join the ends with the galvanometer. This gives us two more solder joints, but they do not interfere as long as they are kept at the same temperature. They must be exceedingly small and

thin, so that the infinitesimal quantity of heat radiated by
the stars will warm the element as much as possible. The
proportions of the whole apparatus are determined by
this requirement. In the thermoelements today in use, the
wires are .001 inch thick (one wire is of bismuth, the
other of an alloy of bismuth and a little tin), and the
solder joints are pressed into hair-thin metal disks of .02
inch diameter. This apparatus, blackened with a particularly effective kind of soot, weighs only .005 grains—
a drop of water weighs a thousand times as much as the
whole thermoelement.

Although the thermoelement is placed in a vacuum,
so the warmth induced may not be dispersed through the
air (there is no way of preventing some loss through the
wires), the most powerful star radiation produces a
temperature increase of only one-hundredth of a degree.
But the sensitivity of the apparatus is so great that
temperature increases of several millionths of a degree
can be measured. Figure 40 is a diagram of a thermocell
placed in a telescope. If we look through the eyepiece we
see the thermoelement as in Figure 41. We now turn the
telescope so that the image of the star disappears behind
one of the solder joints *A* or *B*. At this moment the needle
of the galvanometer moves; we then read or photograph
its largest movement. As in other measurements of bright-

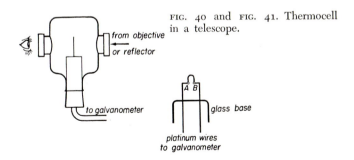

FIG. 40 and FIG. 41. Thermocell in a telescope.

from objective or reflector

to galvanometer

A B

glass base

platinum wires to galvanometer

ness, we can compare different stars with one another and—if we so desire—with earthly sources of radiation.

As we recall from Figure 37, we must not expect the same "brightnesses" for total radiation as for visual or photographic observation. In order to make this quite clear, let us classify in a table the ten "brightest" stars from three different points of view: the first column shows their visual magnitude, the second their radiometric magnitude (total radiation), and the third (computed bolometric magnitude) shows the stars in the order they would have if we could measure their total radiation outside the light-absorbing atmosphere of the earth.

The Ten "Brightest" Stars

I VISUAL MAGNITUDE		II RADIOMETRIC MAGNITUDE		III BOLOMETRIC MAGNITUDE	
Sirius	−1.6	Betelgeuse	−1.7	Sirius	−2.3
Canopus	−0.9	Antares	−1.3	Betelgeuse	−2.2
Alpha		Sirius	−1.3	Antares	−1.8
Centauri	+0.1	Canopus	−1.1	Beta	
Vega	+0.1	Gamma		Centauri	−1.6
Capella	+0.2	Crucis	−1.0	Canopus	−1.6
Arcturus	+0.2	Arcturus	−1.0	Gamma	
Rigel	+0.3	Aldebaran	−0.6	Crucis	−1.5
Procyon	+0.5	Alpha		Arcturus	−1.4
Achernar	+0.6	Centauri	−0.5	Achernar	−1.1
Beta		Capella	−0.4	Rigel	−1.1
Centauri	+0.9	Mira Ceti	−0.2	Spica	−1.0

We shall shortly have more to say on this subject in a different connection. Here, we have brought it up to clarify the notion of brightness. We now know that stars must be compared in terms of the same type of brightness. In catalogues that depict the whole sky, only visual or photographic brightness is used—in recent years principally the latter. It is much harder, however, to determine brightness reliably than it is to determine positions;

the observation of brightness is hampered not only by clouds but even by slight mists that have no effect on the direction of light rays. For this reason, the usual catalogues extend only to the seventh or eighth magnitude; the brightnesses of fainter stars given in the catalogues are based on estimates. For certain selected sectors of the sky, however, measurements of brightness have been carried much further, in special cases beyond the twentieth magnitude.

Variable Stars

Repeated observation of star positions has shown us that in the course of time we may expect changes of position (proper motion) for all stars. The brightness of the stars, however, proves in the main to be invariable. But there are *variable stars*. There is, for instance, Algol in the constellation of Perseus. Ordinarily, Algol is only a little fainter than Algenib, the brightest star in the constellation. But from time to time it suddenly fades. After a little less than 5 hours it is 1½ magnitudes—that is, quite appreciably—fainter than Algenib. Then it begins at once to increase in brightness, and in another 5 hours it has returned to normal. The whole process takes 9½ hours and is repeated punctually every 69 hours. If we note down the times and brightnesses as in Figure 42, we obtain a clear picture of the light change. More patience is needed in the observation of the first variable to

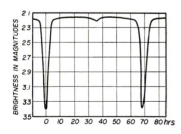

FIG. 42. Light curve of Algol.

be discovered, Omicron Ceti, also known as Mira Ceti ("the miraculous star in the Whale"). Its light changes very slowly and irregularly, and it reaches maximum brightness approximately every 11 months. But the fluctuation is very great (up to 6 magnitudes), so that even in the inconspicuous constellation of Cetus it is noticeable whether or not Mira is visible. Figure 43 gives us a light curve for Mira Ceti; but it should be noted that the curve may differ somewhat from year to year.

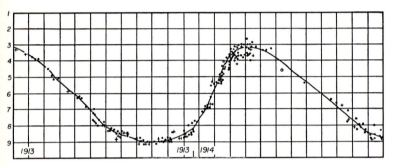

FIG. 43. Light curve of Mira Ceti in the years 1913 and 1914. Horizontally the side of one square signifies 20 days, vertically one magnitude.

We know today several hundred variable stars of one type or another. Besides, there are other kinds of light change. In all, several thousand stars are recognized as variable (those which are not bright are designated by large Roman letters before the name of the constellation). It is not always so easy to establish the light curve as it might appear from our account. Stars can be observed only at night, and even then only when they are fairly high above the horizon and not concealed by clouds (a condition none too frequent in many regions). It follows that we cannot measure the entire light change at one sitting, but must combine observations made at different times and different places. It often takes a long period of trial and error before the observations fall into a pattern. Changes in brightness are observed with great precision, because the variables are compared with other stars in their vicinity and of similar brightness—where possible, some of them a little brighter, others a little fainter. Since in such limited ranges of brightness estimates of degree are very accurate and reliable, this is the field of astronomy in which amateurs have made the greatest contribution.

Variables as Milestones in Space

Figure 44 shows a highly important type of variable. These stars "flare up" briefly at regular intervals, much like beacons. They are called Cepheid variables from Delta Cephei, the first such star to be observed. In Delta Cephei, the period between the two peaks of brightness runs to 5⅓ days, but there are Cepheids with periods of up to 40 days, others with short periods of approximately half a day. The star with the shortest period flares up every hour and a half.

A discovery of the highest importance was made during the studies of the Magellanic Clouds in the southern sky, which turned out to be neighboring stellar systems (p. 186). During these investigations, astronomers came across a great number of Cepheid variables. It was soon noticed that bright stars of this type had long periods of light change, faint ones short periods. If we plot these stars on a graph showing length of period, from left to

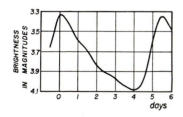

FIG. 44. Light curve of Delta Cephei.

right, mean brightness from the bottom to the top, we discover a consistent relationship between brightness and length of period (Fig. 46).

We must bear in mind that these stars belong to a separate stellar system which we see from a great distance. This means that they are all roughly the same distance away from us, so that the order of their apparent brightness reflects the order of their real brightness. Accordingly, the relation between brightness and period we have discovered reveals a physical connection between two properties in all stars of this kind—between the amount of light constantly emitted and the period in which it fluctuates. We may safely assume that this connection is not peculiar to the Small Magellanic Cloud, but applies generally. Thus, once we determine the period of change in a star that shows light fluctuations of this sort, we can derive its brightness from the curve shown in Figure 46. This method, to be sure, only tells us how

FIG. 45. The smaller of the two Magellanic Clouds in the southern sky. At the upper edge two round star clusters are visible, which are much closer to us than is the cloud (photograph of the Harvard Station in Peru).

bright our star would be if it were in the Small Magellanic Cloud, and that is not very helpful. But even from
this information we can make certain deductions.

Let us assume that the star we have discovered has
a period of 4 days. In the Magellanic Cloud it would
then, by our curve, have a brightness of 17.0. Let us
further assume that we have measured an apparent
brightness of 13.5. This means that the star appears
brighter to us than if it were in the Magellanic Cloud
—it must be nearer to us than the Cloud. How much
farther away the Cloud is must be deducible from the
difference in brightness, since it is known that in the
propagation of light ¼ brightness corresponds to double
the distance (or ⅑ brightness to triple the distance).
Considering further how brightness is expressed in magnitudes, we arrive at a table that shows the relationship.

According to our table the star under observation is
only ⅕ as far away as the Magellanic Cloud. Hence, on

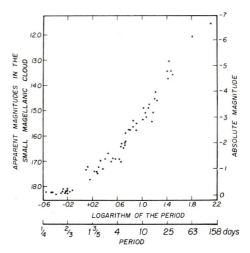

FIG. 46. Relations between period and brightness in the Cepheid variables.

the basis of measurements of brightness, we could determine its distance, and the distances of all Cepheid variables, if only we knew the distance of the small Magellanic Cloud. But this distance proves to be so great, we have no hope of determining it by measuring the parallaxes or the proper motions of stars in the Cloud. We must proceed indirectly.

DISTANCE	DIFFERENCE OF BRIGHTNESS IN MAGNITUDES
twice	1.5
3 times	2.4
4 times	3.0
5 times	3.5
10 times	5.0
100 times	10.0
1000 times	15.0
10,000 times	20.0
100,000 times	25.0
1,000,000 times	30.0

Theoretically, it would suffice to determine by parallax measurement the distance of a single Cepheid variable that is close to us; the difference between its apparent brightness and the brightness corresponding to its period would give us the distance of the Cloud. But, unfortunately, no Cepheid variable is close enough for this purpose. We, therefore, must content ourselves with a statistical determination (p. 55), by attempting to measure the proper motions of as many such stars as possible. The values we obtain for the distance of each of the stars, and hence for the Small Magellanic Cloud, are very inexact—but taken together, a great many such determinations finally add up to give a reliable distance for the Cloud.

Brightness a Measure of Distance After All

To work with the remote Magellanic Cloud whenever

we wished to determine the luminosity of a star is not very convenient. A smaller yardstick would be handier. The light-year is our general standard of distance, but for considerations of brightness we have established a different measure: 33 light-years (more precisely 32.6 light-years, corresponding to a parallax of $\frac{1}{10}$ second of arc). When we compare stars according to real brightness (luminosity), we consider them as transposed to this distance. The magnitude that they would have at this distance we call their absolute magnitude. From absolute magnitude (M) and apparent magnitude (m), distance can always be computed, since the difference between the two can be converted with the help of the table on page 82 into a relation of distance, which tells us how many times 33 light-years the distance amounts to. The table is thus transformed into another table which is still more useful, and which we therefore show a little more fully:

Brightness (Magnitude) and Distance

m — M	DISTANCE (IN LIGHT-YEARS)	m — M	DISTANCE (IN LIGHT-YEARS)
−5	3	+11	5200
−4	5	12	8100
−3	8	13	13,000
−2	13	14	20,000
−1	20	15	33,000
0	33	16	52,000
+1	52	17	81,000
2	81	18	130,000
3	130	19	200,000
4	205	20	326,000
5	325	21	520,000
6	520	22	810,000
7	810	23	1,300,000
8	1300	24	2,000,000
9	2000	+25	3,260,000
+10	3260		

Finally, let us apply this table to the Cepheid variables in the Magellanic Cloud. Their distance corresponds to an m — M of 18.3 magnitudes. Accordingly, if we subtract 18.3 from all the figures on the left edge of our diagram, Figure 46, we shall have the absolute magnitude of the stars in question for all the periods shown. The difference between this and the measured, apparent magnitude leads by a simple computation—here replaced by the table above—to the distance.

The Cepheid variables have played a very special part in our progress to the most distant objects of observation (p. 182). But there are still other methods of obtaining absolute brightness (p. 125), and the utility of brightness for determining distances is not restricted to Cepheid variables. The special importance of these photometric methods of distance measurement is that they need not stop at the limits inherent in other methods (p. 49).

Solar Eclipses Seen from a Great Distance

When we turn to the question of what sort of process produces the light change of the variable stars, one class of variables, the Algol stars, must be considered separately from the others. Here the complete regularity of the light change points to a mechanical process. The periodic decline of brightness reminds us of a solar eclipse. With the Algol stars, however, the eclipse cannot be caused by a moon or planet, for the effects of such small bodies would be imperceptible to us. But we can conceive of a double star system so placed, in relation to us, that in every circuit one of the two stars moves in front of the other. If we assume one star to be non-luminous, no light is lost when it is covered by the bright star; but the nonluminous star wholly or partly extinguishes the light of its bright companion while passing in front of it (Fig. 47). Thus every circuit shows a darkening, which is usually partial. If the companion

FIG. 47. Eclipses of double stars.

star is not dark, we shall have at every circuit two dark-
enings of varying degree. In the case of Algol, delicate
measurements reveal the second minimum (Fig. 42).
Clearly, the total amount and period of such a darkening
allows us to deduce the size of the stars, and the situation
and size of their orbit. The light curve can be translated
into a geometrically correct picture of the binary star
system—though the scale remains unknown. We obtain
the scale only if we can see both stars and measure their
orbit. Here ordinary "seeing" is out of the question, for
the systems are very small, and often the distance between the bodies is not much greater than their diameters. But luckily there is a possibility of observation (p.
128). In some, though unfortunately not very many, cases
we can find out everything we want to know about a
star: diameter (volume, surface), mass, density (= mass :
volume). The following table contains a few of the stars
that could be fully determined; the figures indicate diameter, mass, and density as compared to the diameter,
mass, and density of our sun.

Here as among the visual double stars (p. 55), we
notice the occurrence of smaller, but also considerably
larger, masses than that of our sun. But we also see that,
in these stars at least, the density (quantity of matter per
cubic inch) is almost always less than that of our sun,
which contains roughly as much matter as if it were filled
with water throughout. The last two columns show how
small are the swift orbits of these stars. In some systems
the surfaces almost touch, and it is possible that there
are cases in which the two stars are not quite separated.
It seems likely that such double stars develop from single
stars as a result of shrinkage and the concomitant increase

A Few Eclipsing Variables

STAR	DIAMETER	MASS	MEAN DENSITY	DISTANCE BETWEEN CENTERS	SURFACES
Zeta Aurigae	293.4	31.9	0.000001	744.6	419.3
	4.0	12.9	0.20		
Beta Aurigae	2.9	2.4	0.1	9.0	6.1
	2.9	2.4	0.1		
R Canis Majoris	0.9	0.14	0.19	1.3	0.4
	0.9	0.05	0.07		
YY Geminorum	0.8	0.6	1.2	1.9	1.2
	0.7	0.6	1.7		
Beta Lyrae	18.4	18.7	0.0030	35.4	4.2
	44.0	7.1	0.0005		
Beta Persei (Algol)	3.2	4.6	0.14	7.5	4.1
	3.6	1.0	0.02		
V Puppis	8.3	21.2	0.04	9.0	1.0
	7.6	16.3	0.04		
Lambda Tauri	5.1	13.8	0.10	8.5	4.1
	3.7	2.8	0.06		
W Ursae Majoris	1.0	0.7	0.7	1.1	0.1
	1.0	0.5	0.5		

(in diameters of the sun)

in velocity of rotation. The examination of the spectrum of large hot stars has shown that many of them rotate so fast as to be actually on the verge of flying apart.

Hidden Causes

With the other classes of variables, we have no such clear idea of the process that causes their change of light. The great differences in length and magnitude of the fluctuation, and the wide variety of their light curves make it difficult to find a clue. But with all their diversity, they show certain similarities and gradations, which lead us to believe that the changes in light always arise from the same physical cause, which operates differently according to the conditions prevailing in the star. The

Cepheids, too, show motions, but these stand in different relations to the change of light than the rotary movements of the eclipsing variables. These stars seem alternately to expand and contract, and in so doing to change their temperature and radiation. What provokes these pulsations has not yet been clearly determined; it is still uncertain whether they occur only under special conditions, or whether every star passes into this state in the course of its development.

The "flare stars" are a great riddle (from the flares or eruptions on the sun's surface, hence a particularly bright, hot cloud of gas). Occasionally, and at irregular intervals, a few very faint stars (10,000 times fainter than our sun) exhibit for several minutes enormous increases in brightness (a hundred or more times their normal brightness). The question is whether this is, on a gigantic scale, the same phenomenon as in the sun's protuberances (p. 137). Only the largest telescopes can answer this question. But as a rule it is impractical to aim such telescopes for weeks at a single faint star in the hope of catching an eruption. They are usually taken up with other work.

Novae

Questions of this sort are particularly stimulated by certain stars called new stars or novae. They suddenly emerge out of a state of invisibility (Fig. 48) and become quite conspicuous within a few days or even hours. The first new stars of which we have definite knowledge were literally eye-catching: the "nova" of 1572 could be seen in broad daylight. Today, with the entire sky constantly being photographed, the appearance of a star even of twelfth magnitude is noticed. Although the discovery of a new star is thus no rare event, it nevertheless causes a small upheaval in the astronomical world, for the key to the understanding of the whole process lies in

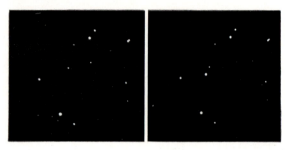

FIG. 48. A nova—in the middle of the right-hand picture (Lippert astrograph of the Hamburg Observatory).

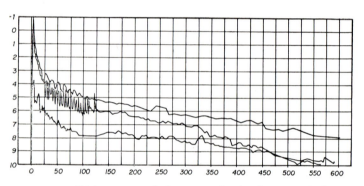

FIG. 49. Light curves of the novae in Aquila in 1918 (upper curve), in Perseus in 1901 (middle curve), and in Gemini in 1917 (lower curve).

the swift succession of events shortly before and after maximum brightness. Once the increase in light has been discovered, not a moment must be lost.

The brighter ones among the new stars can almost always be found as faint stars on earlier photographs. At times they have previously been noted as variables. We know then that in a brief time these stars increase their radiation by at least 7 or 8 magnitudes, or a thousand, ten thousand, or even a hundred thousand times (Fig. 49). What these figures mean will become evident if we imagine that such a transformation was taking place in one of the brighter stars: if Sirius were to become ten thousand times as bright, it would give as much light as the full moon. Various kinds of observation tell us that the increase of radiation is connected with an expansion of the star during which the outer strata move outward at velocities of over 60 miles a second. When maximum brightness is reached, the type of radiation changes. The normal star radiation diminishes and is overlaid by a radiation known to us from the gaseous nebulae. At this time the nova does not appear quite as dotlike as a normal star, and this in itself indicates an immense growth.

As the total brightness decreases slowly and with much fluctuation over a period of months or years, the star's radiation again assumes a character familiar to us. It is

FIG. 50. Nebula surrounding the nova Persei of 1901 (photograph taken in 1938 with the 39-inch reflector of the Hamburg Observatory). Figures 50 and 51 take in the same field of the sky.

not, however, the same kind of radiation as before maximum brightness, but rather that of "nebulous" stars. The star has in fact become a "new" star. In some new stars observed in this century the nebulous covering has in time broken away from the star and moved farther and farther away year after year (Fig. 50). In the great nova of 1901, the light waves that emanated from the star could be seen spreading through a nebulous mass embracing the star (Fig. 51).

We are still far from a full understanding of the meaning of these phenomena, which differ somewhat with every new star. Their cause seems to lie in instabilities in the star's structure, which suddenly bring about an eruption of the surface and the release of great quantities of heat normally confined within the star.

A class in themselves are the supernovae. At their maximum brightness they are as bright as a whole star system. This quality has made it possible to find great numbers of them in a systematic survey of the sky with the 18-inch Schmidt telescope of Mt. Palomar Observatory.

III. COLOR (THE SPECTRUM)

While we were trying by various means to measure the radiation of the stars, we discovered that the light of the stars varies not only in intensity but also in color. At the time this struck us as a bothersome difficulty. But if we take a broader view, this phenomenon offers a road to further knowledge.

The Colors of the Stars

Several examples have already taught us that our eye is capable of distinguishing star colors and arranging them according to a color scale. But since such color estimates show idiosyncrasies, originating both in the ob-

a

b

FIG. 51. Luminous ring around nova Persei (photographs of the Yerkes Observatory; *a* taken on Sept. 30, *b* on Nov. 13, 1901).

server and in his telescope, astronomers have again endeavored to arrive at a more "impersonal" method of observation. The discussion on page 70 leads us to such a method. There we established that the eye and the photographic plate take in different parts of a star's radiation and that the relative amounts depend on the color. The difference between a star's visual and its photographic magnitude is therefore known as its *color index;* it has become the usual measure of star color.

The Color Indices of a Few Bright Stars

STAR	COLOR INDEX	STAR	COLOR INDEX
Sirius	+0.2	Polestar	+0.8
Rigel	—0.2	Arcturus	+1.4
Regulus	0.0	Aldebaran	+1.8
Spica	—0.5	Betelgeuse	+2.0
Capella	+0.9	Antares	+2.0

What Do the Colors of the Stars Mean?

If on our earth the leaves of the trees are green and flowers red, yellow, blue, or violet, it is because every body absorbs a part of the white sunlight falling on it and reflects the rest. Different substances absorb different color segments from the sun's radiation, which contains all colors, and the result is the great diversity of colors in the world around us. The planets of our solar system, visible only because they are illuminated by the sun, obtain their coloration in this way. But the colors of the stars are different; the light we receive from them is not reflected light. They themselves radiate light and heat like the sun.

Our earthly experience tells us that only hot bodies give off light. (There are still other possibilities, as for example the glow of rotting wood, but they are not very important.) All the heat and light radiation that we use emanates from bodies at a high temperature. Now let us try to understand this phenomenon a little better, by an experiment.

Our source of radiation is an iron stove in a cold room. As long as it is not heated, it is a dead object that makes no impression on us. We light a fire in it which is invisible from outside. Inside the stove, there is soon a great heat, but it takes some time to penetrate the lining in the stove. We sit down beside the stove and wait. We turn out the light in the room. This makes us even more uncomfortable, but the road to knowledge is usually a little bothersome. After a while the stove begins to give signs of life. From its direction warmth strikes our hands and face. The sensation grows stronger and stronger and in the end may become unpleasant. If meanwhile we have touched the stove from time to time, we have noticed that it has grown gradually warmer and finally very hot. Up to now we do not see the stove. But we soon shall, if we have made a good hot fire. When the heat radiation has become very intense, the stove gradually appears, a pale-gray ghost (where light impressions are so faint, our eye sees no colors: at night all cats are gray). A little later we see dark red, then bright red, and then the red turns white hot. For this part of the experiment we can use instead a needle held in a gas flame. It passes through all the stages more quickly than the stove, and our observation need not begin until the red-hot stage. Since we are not sensitive to the heat radiated by so small a body, we can safely observe the transition from red to white heat; we can even produce the different colors in turn by shifting the needle from one part of the flame to the other.

The colors of the stars have the same significance: the stars are incandescent bodies of varying temperatures. They are not heated from outside like our needle; they are more like the stove, whose hot interior radiates the heat outward. Accordingly, it should be possible to determine the temperature of the stars by comparing their colors with those of an earthly body that is progressively heated (such as the filament of a light bulb through which an electric current passes). Most earthly bodies, however, would not stand up under such temperatures, and besides we should soon find that color estimates are not exact enough for our purpose. In order to get at the temperature of stars, we must take a little more trouble and devise better means of determining their colors.

The Continuous Spectrum

We have said that white light—sunlight, for example— contains rays of all possible colors. So far we have not proved it. However, it is something that anyone can *see*. Block off the sunlight shining through the window by means of a cardboard disk, with a narrow slit cut in its center. A streak of light will shine into the room and will fall on the opposite wall as a white line (Fig. 52). Now set a prism—a glass wedge—in the streak of light. Any piece of glass with two plane surfaces at an acute angle will function as a prism.

As soon as the prism is in place, the white strip vanishes. Instead there appears a whole rectangle, farther down the wall, red on top, violet below, and white in the middle. As we narrow the slit in the cardboard the white dissolves more and more, and at length we obtain a

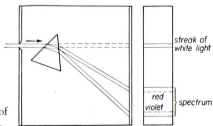

streak of
white light

red
violet } spectrum

FIG. 52. Dispersion of light through a prism.

rectangle composed of red, orange, yellow, green, blue, and violet stripes which are not sharply defined but pass imperceptibly into one another. We call such a band of color a spectrum. If it has been produced by the dispersion of white light, it does not contain every possible color (our present techniques can produce an unbelievable number of colors). But it shows all the simple colors from red to violet—the same colors that show up, a trifle more blurred, in the rainbow produced by the breaking of sunlight in falling raindrops.

To the naked eye, the spectrum falls off into darkness after red and violet. But this is the fault of our eyes. Other means of observation show that there are also rays below the violet and above the red. A photographic plate, for example, is blackened considerably beyond the edge of the violet—in the ultraviolet. We get still further with a quartz prism in place of our glass prism— but at a certain point our spectrum comes to an end. Let me note at once that beyond this limit we can show no star radiation by any other means. Whatever radiation would fall beyond this borderline is stopped by the air that envelops the earth.

Another way to prove that there is radiation beyond the red is to move a thermometer, or better still a thermoelement (p. 74), upward along the wall. We begin in the ultraviolet. The galvanometer will indicate that all along its path heat radiation is striking the wall— until, beyond the red edge of the spectrum, it finally comes to an end. Again we can extend the limit a little by replacing our glass prism with one made of rock salt, which will pass heat rays that glass would stop. For certain investigations this is very important, but for our present purposes it is of little use. If we give up the prism altogether and produce the spectrum in a different way, by means of a "grating," we can move our thermoelement still farther up before the heat radiation ends.

Wave lengths		$1\mu\mu$	$1\overset{\circ}{A}$ $1m\mu$		1μ	$1cm$ $1mm$	$1m$	$1km$
Type of radiation	gamma rays of radium and shortest waves of cosmic radiation		X rays	ultraviolet / visible light	infrared (heat rays)	electrical waves		

FIG. 53. Band showing complete sun radiation ($1\mu =$ 0.001 mm., 1 mμ = 0.001μ, 1Å = 0.0001μ, etc.).

Long before we reach this limit, however, we can replace the thermoelement with an instrument that registers electric waves (Fig. 53).

Waves and Frequencies

By now, we have gone far beyond the limits of our homemade apparatus. But we have found out that white light, with a little help, dissolves into an unbroken sequence of radiations. Toward one end of the sequence, we see them as colors. Elsewhere, we must designate the radiations in some way that is related to their place in the series. We are already familiar with such a way: electric waves, for example, are distinguished by their wave length, or else by the number of crests that pass a given point per second (frequency). Long electric waves are produced by special electrical apparatus (transmitters). The longest waves that are perceptible by their heat effect are shorter than four-hundredths of an inch. Our eye can only perceive waves between 15 and 30 millionths of an inch (which corresponds to a frequency of 375 to 750 million millions); ultraviolet rays and X rays have still shorter waves (and correspondingly higher frequencies). In the observation of star radiation the earth's atmosphere sets the lower limit of .0003 millimeter (1 millimeter = $\frac{1}{25}''$), because the ozone in its upper strata blocks all shorter waves.

Intensity and Type of Radiation Are Relative to Temperature

Our experiments have shown that the temperature of the radiating body determines what segments of the possible radiation it emits. An examination of the spectrum of a source of radiation at different temperatures will clarify this relation. It can be accomplished by certain additions to our apparatus of Figure 52. Outside the slit we place a thin wire, connected by thicker wires with a source of electric current. One of the thick wires is run through a variable resistor so that we may regulate the strength of the current; finally we need an ammeter to measure the current.

We begin our experiment with a high resistance. The current is slight and our fine wire does not even grow warm. Gradually, we reduce the resistance and wait for something to appear on the screen where we catch the spectrum. We shall not have long to wait. We are aware, of course, that as the temperature rises the radiation will first show itself in the form of heat, and so we place the ball of a sensitive thermometer, or a thermoelement, close to the screen, not at the level where we expect the visible spectrum but above it. As we gradually reduce the resistance, and reach a certain intensity of current, the thermoelement shows that it has been heated by radiation. The more we increase the current and with it the temperature of our wire, the more radiation the thermoelement will register.

At length the moment comes when we can see something: a red strip appears on the screen—a red image of the filament which can now be seen to glow red. The red strip grows brighter and more luminous; it broadens downward, and the descending edge is soon no longer red but yellowish. As it continues to broaden, green is added, and finally—always by way of in-between shades —blue and violet. By this time the wire glows white.

All the while the radiation registered by the thermo-element has mounted: the total quantity of radiation increases with the temperature, and at the same time shorter and shorter waves are added to the initial, long ones. In the end the shorter waves predominate, but very high temperatures must be attained before the greatest intensity of radiation moves into the blue or violet.

Although the relations between radiation and temperature are very clear they are not simple. It took a thorough investigation of radiation phenomena before scientists arrived at the formulae by which we derive for any temperature either the intensity of radiation in a given wave length, or the wave length with the strongest radiation, or the total amount of radiation. The results can be shown in a diagram—Figure 54 does so for four different temperatures. Every temperature has its curve. The intensity of the radiation at a given wave length is shown by the elevation of the curve at this wave length. Wave lengths are indicated by the figures placed at equal intervals below the base line. In our diagram the whole numbers mean wave lengths of 0.001, 0.002, . . . , 0.006 millimeter. The curves drop sharply toward the short

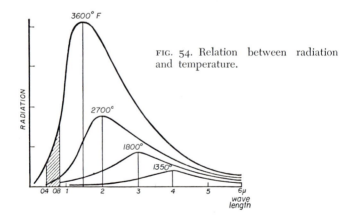

FIG. 54. Relation between radiation and temperature.

wave lengths; this shows how small the part of the spectrum visible as light (from 0.0004 to 0.0008 milli-meter) is in relation to the total radiation, even at tem-peratures as high as 3500°. At higher temperatures, a maximum of radiation passes through the visible seg-ment as is shown in Figure 37 (p. 71), where the wave lengths are given in Ångstrom units (1 Å = 0.0000001 millimeter). The curves represent the radiation of a standard source of certain conventional properties. The radiation of natural objects may differ considerably from our standard, but that of the stars is relatively close to the norm.

Now We Can Determine the Temperature of the Stars

At last we know enough about radiation to do what we set out to do: determine the temperature of the stars. The simplest method is to obtain a spectrum of our star, to measure the intensity of the radiation at different points, and so to find out at what wave length the radi-ation is strongest. Then we look through our collection of curves to relate this wave length to the corresponding temperature (actually, we compute it). Since the posi-tion of the maximum radiation is decisive for the effect on the eye or the photographic plate, the color index (p. 92), which is easier to determine, should also give us an indication of the temperature of stars.

At times—for instance where the temperatures are very high—it is impossible to ascertain the maximum radiation. Nor is it necessary. By measuring the intensity of radiation for a fairly good-sized segment of the spec-trum, and noting down the values, we can construct a clear curve and compute the temperature whose radia-tion curve our segment fits. We shall not go into the difficulties arising from the deviations of star radiation from normal radiation; let me say, however, that these deviations are not merely troublesome—they also give us certain information regarding the nature of the stars' atmospheres.

The star temperatures at which we arrive by these methods are very high. The coldest—and therefore the reddest—stars have approximately the same temperature as the incandescent filament of an electric light bulb (3600°), and the hottest white stars show temperatures in the vicinity of 55,000°. Hence there is no way of comparing the spectra of all stars directly with the spectrum of some earthly source of radiation. For the high temperatures, we depend on our trust in the laws of radiation.

The laws of radiation also tell us the total radiation that a given body emits at a given temperature. Since total radiation (or certain parts of it) is what we measure when we determine the brightness of a star with a thermoelement, a photometer, or photographically, we might expect to learn a good deal about the temperature of the stars by those methods. Unfortunately, this is not the case. As we review our law of radiation we soon see why. The temperature determines how much radiation per square inch of surface a body gives off; but the total radiation depends on the size of the body, and about the size of most of the stars we know nothing.

About the sun, however, we are well informed; we can compute its surface, and its total radiation is powerful enough to be measured by its very distinct heating effect. But even so it takes a great deal of thought and calculation before we can say how much radiation per square inch of surface it emits and that its surface must therefore have a temperature of almost 11,000° F. For the stars, we lack most of the information that we have for the sun. What seems most discouraging at first is that we know the distance of only a few of them. But, strange as it may seem, we do not need to know the distance. The only thing we absolutely must know is a star's apparent diameter, that is, the angle formed by lines connecting its top and its bottom edge with our eye. Once we know this, we can compute its real diameter and hence its true surface for any given distance. To compute the total radiation it would send if it were as close to us as the sun, we divide the measured radiation by the square of the distance; and on the other hand, we compute the surface of the star (assuming it to be a sphere) from the angle diameter by multiplying it by the square of the distance. These two operations thus cancel each other out.

What sort of angle diameter may we expect? The sun is almost 100 million miles away; if it were a star 100 trillion miles (15 light-years) away, it would still be among the stars closest to us. But at such a distance its diameter would also appear a million times smaller than now—it would look as large as a small coin at a distance of 1000 miles. We can compute that this amounts to an angle of 0.002 second of arc, but we can see or measure it no longer. There are stars that are much larger than the sun and therefore take up a much more noticeable space in the sky, yet not one of them is large and near

Diameters and Surface Temperatures of a Few Stars

STAR	APPARENT DIAMETER IN SECONDS OF ARC	EFFECTIVE TEMPERA- TURE (F)	DISTANCE IN LIGHT-YEARS	TRUE DIAMETER
Arcturus	0.022	7500	38	27 × sun
Aldebaran	0.020	7000	57	37
Antares	0.040	6000	160	210
Betelgeuse	0.047	6000	270	410
Beta Pegasi	0.021	5500	160	110
Alpha Herculis	0.021	6000	470	320
Omicron Ceti (Mira)	0.056	4500	250	450

enough to appear as more than a point in the telescope. By a particularly cunning method, however, we have succeeded in increasing the magnifying power of the telescope and measuring the apparent diameter of a few stars; of these we can give the effective temperatures.

The Size of the Stars

For the stars listed in the preceding table we also know the distance, and thus we can compute their true size. Some of them are suns so large that the earth's orbit would fit inside them (the diameter of the earth's orbit is 215 times the diameter of the sun). If Betelgeuse or Mira were as close to us as Alpha Centauri, they would show up in our telescope as little disks. These stars, we may assume, are among the largest suns in existence— which makes it seem unlikely that we shall ever succeed in measuring the apparent diameter, and thus the temperature, of very many stars. But the reverse method might perhaps have some value. If we have determined the temperature of a star in some other way (p. 99), we

Average Diameters of Stars

	SPECTRAL CLASS	DIAMETER
Giants	M	42 × sun
	K	15
	G	9
	F	4
	B	8
	A	2
Dwarfs	F	1.4
	G	1.0
	K	0.7
	M	0.5
White dwarfs (See p. 123.)		0.005

can tell its apparent diameter from its measured brightness; and if we also know its distance, we can tell its
true diameter. Thus, indirectly we may gain a general
idea of the sizes prevailing in the world of stars. Our
sun, it turns out, is among the smallest of the stars, but
only a few stars are as much as one hundred times as
large in diameter. The preceding table gives the mean
values for certain classes of stars (p. 118). It should be
noted that there are many times more dwarfs than giants
among the stars.

Gaps in the Spectrum

Thus far, everything we have learned from the spectrum about the stars has rested on the assumption that
the spectrum is an unbroken band of color. There are
such spectra. A wire raised to white heat will produce
an unbroken (continuous) spectrum. But a glance at the
star spectra in Figure 61 shows at once that the spectra
of the heavenly bodies look otherwise. They show gaps—
some broad ones and a good many narrow ones. What
does this mean?

In Figure 55, *T* is an astronomical telescope. The rays
coming from a star fall parallel to one another through
object glass *O* and are gathered into an image of the star
in the focus. From this luminous point, which for us
takes the place of the star, the rays go on and are again
made parallel by a lens. Now a mirror directs them to
another lens, which once more gathers them into a luminous point at *P* on a photographic plate. The point at
P is an image of the star at *S*. If we point our telescope
at the sun and from the disk-shaped sun image at *S* cut
out a narrow strip by means of a slit, we shall obtain
on plate *P* an image of the slit: a thin bright line (dark
on the plate).

If we remove the mirror and in its place set a prism
between the two lenses of the spectrograph, we again

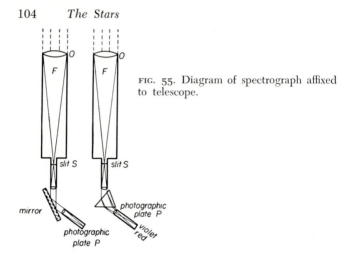

FIG. 55. Diagram of spectrograph affixed to telescope.

obtain an image of the slit as before. This time, however, we find that rays of different wave lengths separate on entering the prism and continue on to *P* by different paths. Consequently, there is at *P* not one image of *S* but a whole series of images (violet rays are refracted more than red ones). Thus, the spectrum consists of a number of images of the slit, side by side, each of them produced by rays of a definite wave length. This series of images is continuous if the light under examination contains all the wave lengths. If there are gaps in the spectrum, it means that the images belonging to certain wave lengths are missing, and we must assume that these wave lengths are not present in the radiation of our light source.

The Line Spectra of the Chemical Elements

How shall we interpret this phenomenon? Have some wave lengths been stopped on their way to us, or are certain rays lacking at the very source of light? It can easily be shown that not every source of light sends out a continuous radiation. Take an alcohol burner or the

FIG. 56. Direct vision pocket spectroscope.

flame of a gas stove. These flames do not give much light, but if we sprinkle salt on them they flare up bright yellow. If we examine this yellow flame with a spectroscope (a direct vision pocket spectroscope is most convenient —Figure 56), we are in for a surprise. There is not a sign of a continuous spectrum. All we see is a single yellow line, at the place where the brightest yellow would be in the continuous spectrum. We must conclude that the salt flame radiates only in a single wave length; the sodium atom that produces the radiation can only vibrate in this rhythm (common salt consists of sodium and chlorine atoms). The same is true of all chemical elements when they are in a gaseous state. Their spectra consists of single lines; some show a few, some a great many. The spectrum of iron vapor, for example, shows several thousand lines (Figure 57). The spectrum of solid or liquid bodies, however, is continuous, because their atoms are pressed so close together that they lose their freedom of motion and cannot radiate in the way natural to them.

Line spectra allow us to recognize elements when a chemical analysis is not possible. Where we see the yellow sodium line, which when strongly magnified proves to be double, we may be sure that sodium is present. A red line and a broad violet line are characteristic of potas-

FIG. 57. Segment of line spectrum of iron over spectrum of Arcturus.

sium. But even these elements show many other lines in addition. When a spectrum shows many lines, two different elements may both have a line in the same place. But since there will be no agreement in the other lines, the spectra of different elements can always be distinguished. Thus, the line spectrum tells us which elements are present in the source of radiation. But it tells us still more. If, for instance, the glowing gas that is the source of light is put under greater pressure, the lines grow broader and blur; their brightness, too, may change. Since the effect on different lines may be very different, the spectrum tells us the density of gases, even if they are on the surface of a star.

The most striking effect upon the spectrum is caused by temperature. We know that noticeable radiation begins only at a certain temperature, and that—given a substance capable of producing a continuous spectrum— the spectrum spreads with rising temperature from infrared into the visible segment, and thence through violet to ultraviolet. Similarly, all the lines of incandescent gases do not appear at once as soon as a certain temperature is reached. Even a single element shows at first only some of its lines, others appear only at a much higher temperature. At very high temperatures the gas atoms lose their cohesion, and one of the tiny particles (electrons) that in some way move around the nucleus of the atom may fly off. When this happens, the atom's radiation changes completely. The spectrum lines of an atom that has lost one or more electrons are entirely different from those of the complete atom. The broad calcium lines H and K in Figure 61, for example, are produced not by the usual "neutral" atom but by an "ionized" atom. How many atoms are complete and how many are not and what lines do appear and at what intensity depend chiefly on the temperature and the density at the source of radiation. Evidently, the spectrum can tell us a

good deal about the stars' atmospheres. But the interpre-
tation of the observed facts is uncommonly difficult, because we are dealing with extremely complex relations.
Even the facts so far outlined are not so simple as they
look; they require a considerable share of the knowledge
gained by modern physics.

The Dark Lines in the Spectrum

What caught our attention most in looking at the sun
spectrum was not the bright lines but the gaps—the dark
lines. Examining spectra that do not have too many lines
(such as A_0, Figure 61), we notice that these dark lines
show the same arrangement as the bright lines of certain
elements (Fig. 58). Measurement shows them to appear
at exactly the same positions in the spectrum.

Let us procure a source of white light, an incandescent
solid body of which we know that it can radiate all colors
—an electric light bulb, for example. Beside it we place
a sodium flame. A pocket spectroscope will suffice to
show us what happens. If we look at the light bulb
through the spectroscope, we obtain the continuous spectrum that was to be expected, with all the colors side by
side from red to violet. Turning our spectroscope toward
the sodium flame, we see the yellow sodium line with
which we are familiar. But let us now place the sodium
flame in front of the light bulb and look into it with our

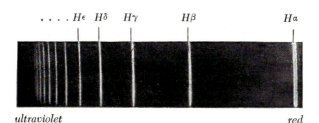

ultraviolet   *red*

FIG. 58. Hydrogen spectrum.

spectroscope. What we now see is different. The continuous spectrum is there, passing through the sodium flame. The sodium line is there, too—but it appears as a dark line in the yellow part of the continuous spectrum.

How does this come about? We must think of it in this way: The special response of the sodium atoms to this particular yellow light is a kind of resonance such as we find in music. Every string of a piano, for example, has a definite tone, in accordance with its length and its tension. If we strike the string, this is the tone it produces. If we send a tone into the piano, for example with a flute, only the one string that is attuned to the note of the flute will swing in response (provided we press the pedal that releases the damper). In a similar fashion, the atoms of the hot sodium vapor pick the special yellow light out of the light of our bulb. They do not, however, absorb it for good. They send it out again, but scatter it in all directions, so that when we look through the flame we see only a part of the yellow light, and this part of the spectrum becomes darker for us.

If we gradually darken the lamp, by reducing the current the temperature of the sodium flame will finally be higher than that of the wire in the lamp. At that point, the radiation of the sodium flame will predominate, and the line will appear bright in the multicolored spectrum.

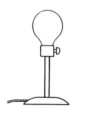 

FIG. 59. Absorption in incandescent gas.

The Sun's Spectrum

Now we are ready to take a look at the spectrum of the sun. It is continuous like that of a solid body. The sun, however, is bound to be surrounded by an atmosphere just as the earth is surrounded by its cover of air, and through this layer of gas the continuous radiation has to pass before it can start on its journey through space. Since every gas absorbs the wave lengths in which it can itself radiate, dark lines appear in the spectrum for those gases that are present in the sun's atmosphere. They are not wholly dark; but their remaining brightness does not, as in our laboratory experiment, correspond to the temperature of the sun strata that produce them, because the radiation mechanism of such thin gases is entirely different.

The sun spectrum is enormously rich in lines (more than 60,000 lines are known), and it is almost hopeless to pick out those that belong together and so to recognize the elements. Only exact measurements can help. We must photograph greatly distended sun spectra and measure the wave lengths of their lines—and in the laboratory we must determine the wave lengths of the lines characteristic for each element. In this way the lines of some 50 elements have been detected in the sun. Hence we are sure that these elements are present in the sun's atmosphere—but we cannot say that other elements do not occur in the sun. An element may be lacking in the atmosphere and yet be present inside the sun; or it may be present in such small quantities that its absorption leaves no visible trace.

We know further that temperature, density, and sometimes other conditions determine whether an element appears, and which of its possible spectra it shows. Hence it may be that we cannot establish the presence of a certain element in the sun merely because its lines fall in a part of the sun spectrum that we cannot observe—for instance, in the ultraviolet that is absorbed by the earth's atmosphere. Since this is the case of most of the missing elements, we may safely assume that nearly all the elements are present in the sun. Their proportions seem to be similar to those on the earth. The proportions cannot simply be read out of the spectrum, because equal quantities of different elements do not produce spectral lines of equal number and equal intensity. The thousands of iron lines, for example, do not mean that there is an overwhelming amount of iron in the sun's atmosphere; they indicate only that the iron atom under such conditions is capable of radiating precisely in all these visible wave lengths. But close study of radiation processes has shown that the intensity and the appearance of the lines bear some relation to the quantity of atoms involved. As far as we have been able to compute this very complex relation, we find on the sun proportions similar to those on earth. An exception is hydrogen, a component of water and of many chemical compounds in the plant and animal world. Though this gas is plentiful even on earth, it is altogether predominant in the atmosphere of the sun.

Iron Vapor in the Sun's Atmosphere

All the elements that we find in the solar spectrum occur in gaseous form. Bright spectral lines (emission) as well as dark ones (absorption) can come only from gases. Even substances as compact as iron, nickel, and other metals, which we can melt only at considerable trouble, pervade the sun's atmosphere just as nitrogen and oxygen occur in the earth's atmosphere. This need not surprise us. The sun's surface (photosphere) from which the radiation with continuous spectrum comes, has, as we know, a temperature of roughly 11,000° F., and we also know that at such great heat the heaviest metals do not just melt—they evaporate (iron melts at 2700° and boils at

5400°). On the surface of the sun such temperatures would not even be necessary to keep these elements in a gaseous state. The boiling points we know apply to conditions on earth where the air column standing over the liquids exerts that pressure which we call "atmosphere." On top of a mountain 20,000 feet high, water will boil at 176°; and if we seal a boiler and keep removing the steam with a powerful pump, we can make water boil at very low temperatures. Even in the lowest layer of the sun's atmosphere, pressure is very slight, because though the atmosphere is extremely deep it is of very low density. In our barometers, air pressure forces the mercury 30 inches up the tube—the sun's atmosphere would not push it up even half an inch (that is, if mercury weighed as much on the sun as it does on earth). Under such conditions, water would evaporate completely at 50°, and where the pressure is so slight even substances that do not readily vaporize pass into a gaseous state at much lower temperatures than on earth. Hence it is no cause for surprise that all these elements occur as gases in the sun's atmosphere.

Is the Sun a Sphere of Gas?

What picture can we form of the sun's "surface" of which we have spoken so glibly? At a temperature of 11,000° it can be no more solid than the layers of atmosphere above it. Of course, the pressure rises as we pass through the "surface" into the interior. But the temperature also rises, and it would quickly turn any liquid into vapor. To look for a solid or liquid core under the sun's atmosphere, analogous to the core of the earth, would obviously be a mistake. All indications are that the sun is gaseous throughout, a great ball of gas. The fact that we see a sharply outlined sun and not a blur of gas does not argue to the contrary. For several reasons there is so sudden a drop in brightness at a certain stratum that the *optical* limit becomes a sharp edge. Nor does the continuous spectrum imply that the sun must be in a liquid or solid state. Inside a large mass of gas (unless it is of uncommonly low density) there develops a radiation in which all wave lengths occur more or less as they do in a "normally" radiating solid body. What we take for the surface is the outermost stratum of the sun from which such radiation reaches us. The atmosphere around it is transparent—except in the wave lengths characterized by the spectral lines.

Some of us may have difficulty with the idea of a gas ball. Our experience with gases—which always expand and escape if we do not lock them up in containers—leads us to suppose that a gas ball would inevitably keep on expanding until it is dissolved completely. But the earth's atmosphere, which is not shut up, does not escape. Actually, it is confined—not by walls but by the gravitation of the earth, which invisibly but firmly binds all the whirling air molecules to its own center, so that only a few at the very edge of the atmosphere succeed occasionally in escaping. Exactly the same holds true for a ball of gas hovering in space. Its particles of matter are held together by gravitation. This acts as a force of attraction between all particles, strong among neighbors, more feeble at a distance—but the general effect is that of a force drawing everything toward the center of the ball. On earth, we know this pull of attraction as weight, and usually note it as a pressure downward, that is, toward the center of the earth.

In the sun, the outer layers press against the inner. Let us try to imagine a smaller sphere inside the sun. It will be compressed by the weight of the layers of gas around it until the increasing tension of the enclosed mass of gas matches the outward pressure. This "tension" with which the enclosed gas opposes the outward pressure may be imagined as though the gas atoms of the inner sphere, always in motion, were delivering blows just powerful enough to resist the pressure from outside each time they came to the outer limit of their sphere. The greater the outside pressure, the more such blows are needed to keep the "ceiling" from falling in. And the faster the atoms move about, the more frequent become the thrusts. The average velocity of the atoms, now, is what we measure as temperature! All at once, we understand that it is possible to know something about the temperature inside the sun, even though we can see only its outermost layers.

The Inside of the Stars

We shall leave it to the mathematicians and physicists to reach into the middle of the sun and take its temperature, and shall take their word for the result: approximately 35 million degrees F. We need not take the figure too literally. To the astrophysicist it is not altogether indifferent whether it is actually 15 or 45 million, but to our imagination these figures all mean the same thing— inconceivable heat. Actually, the heat is inconceivable only if we try to imagine how uncomfortable it would make us—such notions make sense only in the low temperatures with which we are familiar.

Conceived in terms of physics, it is a different matter. We recall that temperature indicates the velocity at which the molecules move (on an average—some always move slower, others more quickly). How great are these velocities? At normal room temperature, the average velocity of the air molecules is about 1600 feet per second. Each air molecule could fly this distance in a second if it did not at once collide with another molecule. This speed is two to three times that of fast passenger planes, though less than the muzzle velocity of a rifle bullet.

At a temperature of 36 million degrees, the velocity of the atoms is still less leisurely. The average then becomes approximately 60 miles a second. Such speeds are beyond the limits of the familiar—a train needs a full hour to cover such a distance—but they are still not completely outside our experience. The shooting stars that we see darting through our atmosphere at night often have a velocity of 60 miles a second. Also, we remember that the earth must cover almost 20 miles a second in order to travel round the sun in a year, and that the entire solar system races through space at 12 miles a second. There is a substance that is called radium because it emits a great variety of radiations. Whole particles fly out of it, nuclei of the element helium, at a speed of 10,000 miles a second, and electrons at a speed of as much as 100,000 miles a second. This element is used in laboratories and hospitals. What we find in the sun, then, is not quite so startling and inconceivable as we thought.

The headlong movement of the atoms that produces the sun's internal temperature is necessary, however, to withstand the pressure of the outer layers. Even so, it cannot prevent the sun from being compressed. The deeper that we penetrate the sun's interior, the greater the outside weight and the more tightly the gas is compressed. If we consider that a mass of matter 375,000 miles in height—enough to make 300,000 of our earths—presses upon the center of the sun from all sides, we begin to get an idea of the immense pressures that prevail in the interior of this gas ball, and we also begin to have some doubts as to the gaseous state of the center of such a ball. In addition, the average density of the sun is 1½ times as great as that of water in its liquid state, and since the outer layers are extremely "airy" the innermost strata must have very considerable density.

It is hard for us to conceive of a gas that will compress as much matter into a cubic foot as if it were solid iron. What we call gas is the state of matter in which there is so much empty space between the atoms that they can fly a little way before they collide with a fellow atom; and this is not the case at the density of solid and liquid bodies. An atom is not a billiard ball, of course, but a very complicated structure with a small solid nucleus and a greater or lesser number of tiny electrons—according to the type of atom—which in their motion around the nucleus take up a certain amount of space. Into this space nothing can penetrate from outside. It determines the size of the normal atom, and once the atoms touch at the limits of these spaces, gas ceases to be compressible and the liquid state is reached.

At very high temperatures, however, atoms behave differently. They collide often and very violently, and in these collisions it happens frequently that an electron flies out of the atom, to continue its career by itself (it may in the end be captured by another atom). If there are many electrons in the atom, several may fly off. The harder the collisions—in other words, the higher the temperature—the more frequently the entire envelope of electrons is scattered, so that at last only the atomic nucleus remains. Atomic nuclei are much smaller than the complete atoms and can move much closer together under great pressure. In that case there will actually be as much "mass" in a cubic foot of gas as in an equally large lump of iron at a low temperature—yet the atomic nuclei and electrons remain mobile, so that the characteristic of gases, compressibility, remains. How incredibly tight atoms can be packed under certain conditions is shown by a few "dense" stars: all our calculations force upon us the conclusion that a thimbleful of matter from the interior of these stars would on earth weigh over a hundred pounds. Whether a gaseous state is maintained at this density we do not know.

Theory and Observation Go Hand in Hand

Why is it so important to know that the sun is gaseous all the way through? Not so very long ago nobody bothered much about the question, but when it had gradually become clear that the sun was gaseous, scientists began to see how helpful this fact could be. In a gas, everything happens in the simplest and clearest way and according to determinable rules: temperature, density, pressure, radiation bear known relations to each other. Whatever we want to know about a sphere of gas we can compute. From the sun's size and mass, we can deduce the density, pressure, and temperature in all its strata, from the surface down to the center.

We know that the temperature determines the intensity and type of radiation in the various parts of the sun, and the amount of radiation that emerges can be verified by observation. It is less simple, of course, to follow the course of radiation through the whole sun to the surface, for at every step it is absorbed, to reappear transformed. Our attempts to pursue our inquiries ever more deeply toward the sun's center require certain assumptions whose soundness we cannot prove, but which seem plausible to those who are thoroughly familiar with all the aspects of the problem. And when in the end it turns out that the sun actually has the brightness that our computations demand, it seems legitimate to assume that our ideas about conditions inside the sun are by and large correct.

Still, our calculations may not be exactly right. We may have "guessed wrong" in regard to this or that property of matter under conditions unfamiliar to us. Fortunately, we can test our theories on certain other suns. We know the mass of only a few stars (p. 86), and the luminosity (absolute magnitude) of fewer still (p. 83). Where both are known, however, we can carry out the same computation as for the sun. Fortunately, our ap-

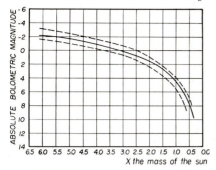

FIG. 60. Relation between mass and absolute magnitude of stars.

proximate knowledge of the stars' diameter is sufficient for the purpose. The results are shown in Figure 60.

Any point inside the rectangle in Figure 60 could correspond to a star. Its absolute brightness we read on the vertical scale, its mass on the horizontal scale. But not all stars that are possible do in fact occur. Almost all of the stars that exist in nature lie in the narrow band between the dotted lines. The reason lies in the physical properties of matter; and the shape of the solid line in Figure 60, along which all stars should lie by our computations, shows that our theoretical assumptions about the properties of matter cannot be too far off. One of these assumptions is that the chemical composition of the sun's interior is about the same as that in its atmosphere, and that roughly one-third of its entire matter must be hydrogen. The same holds for almost all the stars whose mass, diameter, and absolute brightness we know accurately enough to make such a calculation. The great majority of the stars would seem to be composed in this way, though there must certainly be other stars that deviate from this norm.

Different Kinds of Stars

It is strange that there should be so much uniformity among the stars. At first sight we should rather expect the opposite. Let us look at the spectra of a few stars. Figure 61 shows the spectra of 14 of them—the differ-

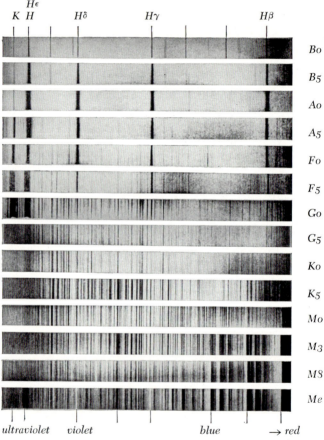

FIG. 61. Types of star spectra (from photographs of the University of Michigan Observatory).

FIG. 62. Spectrum of a gaseous nebula (photograph of the Lick Observatory).

violet

red

FIG. 63. Telescope with objective prism.

ence between the top and the bottom spectra is certainly striking. Looking at the spectra more closely, we notice that, in the arrangement in our table, they form a regular series; each spectrum is very similar to the one preceding it, yet every step in the series brings new dissimilarities. A table of this sort did not always exist. Several thousand spectra had to be examined before we knew the range of possibilities. Still, there are stars whose spectra show no resemblance to any in our table, but they are rare compared with the vast number of the "normal" stars whose spectra fit into our series. What is important here is that there are also spectra which consist of nothing but bright lines. These must come from masses of very thinly distributed gas. They cannot have the structure of a star, in which the density increases greatly toward the center (Fig. 62).

The examples in Figure 61 are called *spectral types*, known by the symbols shown on the right of the table. The simplest are clearly the spectra of type A_0 (and their neighbors B_5 and A_5. They show a series of broad lines, arranged in a way that is easily identifiable. On celestial photographs on which a large prism placed before the object glass (Fig. 63) draws every star out into a spectrum (Fig. 64), the A-stars are also the easiest to find. A glance at Figure 58 shows that the broad lines are pro-

FIG. 64. A spectrum plate prepared with the Lippert astrograph of the Hamburg Observatory. On such plates the spectrum lines can be seen clearly under the microscope.

duced by hydrogen; their remarkable rhythmic sequence with decreasing intervals, ending in a sharp edge in the violet, stems from the properties of the hydrogen atom.

The hydrogen spectrum is dominant also in spectra of the B_0 type. But other lines appear as well, coming chiefly from helium. Downward on our chart, the hydrogen lines remain distinct till F_5, but from F_0 on there appears many other lines which become more and more numerous and intense in subsequent types. For a while, the two thick calcium lines H and K, at the violet end of the spectrum, remain prominent (almost exactly at the same place as H there is also a hydrogen line); then the innumerable metal lines begin to predominate, iron alone contributing several thousands. Beginning with K_5 we find a new phenomenon, groups of lines that begin with a sharp edge and then quickly, though growing fainter by degrees, merge with the general spectrum. Such bands, as we know from the laboratory, are emitted by molecules of chemical compounds, and accordingly they cannot occur at very high temperatures.

There is a catalogue in which the spectra of 225,000

stars are recorded; it contains all stars down to the eighth magnitude, and a considerable number of fainter ones besides. We shall get a notion of how much time, effort, and devotion went into the making of this catalogue when we consider that it was necessary to photograph all the fields of the sky with an object prism (Fig. 63), to examine every single line on each of these photographs, and to classify them according to spectrum tables. Today we can photograph the spectra of much fainter stars; but there are such swarms of them that we can examine only small selected fields of the sky.

From what has been said about how line spectra are produced, we would assume that the diversities in star spectra are related to the physical conditions prevailing in the star's atmosphere, first of all by its temperature. The assumption is correct. B and A stars are white, G stars yellow, K and M stars reddish. For the moment let us look only at the figures under "Main Series":

Spectral Type and Temperature

SPECTRUM	COLOR INDEX		EFFECTIVE TEMPERATURE	
	MAIN SERIES	GIANTS	MAIN SERIES	GIANTS
Bo	−0.2	...	45,000°	...
Ao	0.0	...	19,800	...
Fo	+0.4	+0.4	22,500	...
Go	+0.6	+0.7	10,800	9400
Ko	+0.9	+1.2	8,800	7200
Mo	+1.5	+1.8	6,300	5500

Color, we know, indicates the relations of intensity in the continuous spectrum, and hence the temperature at the "surface" of the star (p. 111). When we take the stars whose temperatures are known, sort them according to spectral types, and then determine the average temperature for each type, the figures in the above table are the result.

There is, then, nothing surprising in the diversity of the spectra. The atoms of the various gases radiate differently at 36,000° and at 5000°; at high temperatures, some of the atoms have lost one or two electrons, and then radiate at entirely different wave lengths. Moreover, among all the possible variations we see only those that fall within the small part of the spectrum we can see or photograph. Thus, the varying occurrence of the different elements in the spectra is just what we would have to expect.

The Nearest Stars

The stars closest to us furnish certain observations that are not self-explanatory. Figure 65 shows 53 known stars within the range of 16 light-years. This zone contains stars from the first to the sixteenth absolute magnitude, that is, ranging from 40 to $\frac{1}{25,000}$ times as bright as the sun. But here again, we do not find every conceivable sort of star. The dots which in Figure 65 represent stars lie, with only a few exceptions, in a narrow band running from the upper left to the lower right. The white A stars radiate great quantities of energy, the red M stars radiate only slightly. According to the relation shown in Figure 60, this means that the white stars have greater mass than the red ones. But there are exceptions, as the stars

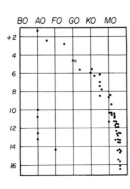

FIG. 65. Spectrum and luminosity: the nearest stars ($\times$ = the sun).

at the lower left of the figure make clear. These have too little brightness for their spectral type and the surface temperature that goes with it—hence they must be much smaller than the usual stars of the same spectral classes at the top of the diagram. But their mass is not proportionately smaller, as we know from the companion of Sirius (p. 58). And so we reach the surprising conclusion that the matter in them must be uncommonly dense. These stars are called "*white* dwarfs." They emit so little light that they easily escape notice. After a good deal of hunting for them we now know some 120 such white dwarfs. We can find them only when they are very close to us, and great proximity is most easily deduced from large proper motion. For example, a star that is not very far away, moving with a velocity of 10 miles a second obliquely to our line of sight, shows conspicuous proper motion. Most white dwarfs have thus been identified as faint stars with large proper motions. They would seem to be much more numerous than we formerly supposed.

The Brightest Stars: Giants and Dwarfs

If we extend our field of investigation and survey the hundred stars within a range of 32 light-years, the results are similar. Figure 66 (which otherwise parallels Figure 65) includes the brightest stars (the stars with the greatest *apparent* brightness) in the sky. Some of the stars from the 16 light-year zone are still present; the less luminous ones are missing, because with all their closeness they are not bright enough to be counted among the brightest. On the other hand, there is a considerable number of well-known stars that do not occur in Figure 65 because they are farther—some of them much farther—than 16 light-years away.

The main series of stars shows up again in the diagram of the brightest stars; but there are other groups as well. There is the group of the G, K, and M stars, to which

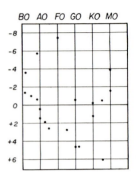

FIG. 66. Spectrum and luminosity: the brightest stars.

belong Capella, Arcturus, Antares, and Aldebaran. Their absolute brightness is greater than that of the brightest stars of the main series. Since they are stars of lesser surface temperature, they must be large. They are giants compared with the dwarfs in the main series that belong to the same spectral classes. The B stars (at the left of the diagram, absolute brightness of −2 and −1) have nearly the same luminosity. Despite their great brightness and mass these stars are not as large as the red giants; their powerful radiation comes from their high temperature. But the "super giants," the brightest of which emits 50,000 times as much radiation as the sun, must be colossal in both mass and size.

Distance Determined by the Spectrum

The spectra of large stars and small stars are not exactly alike because the density of the gas in the absorbing strata of the star atmosphere is not the same. Giants have for the most part sharper lines than dwarfs; in addition, there are lines that appear only in giants, and not in dwarfs with otherwise identical spectra. Some lines are more intense in giants than in dwarfs, and of other lines the opposite is true. For some lines these differences are so pronounced that we can deduce from them the luminosity of the stars. This fact is more important than may at first appear.

The possibility of deducing luminosity from the spectrum gives us nothing new as long as we are dealing with the stars of our immediate vicinity, whose distances can be measured with the usual surveying methods (trigonometric parallaxes). These known distances, and the absolute brightnesses of nearby stars which we derive from them, are in fact needed to establish the key by which differences of intensity in the spectral lines can be translated into absolute brightnesses. But once we have this key, we can determine the absolute brightness and distance of any star that is bright enough to have a serviceable spectrum, regardless of how far away it may be. The direct method of measuring distance, on the other hand, can be used only up to distances of roughly 150 light-years, and most of the bright stars are beyond this zone. Spectroscopic parallax, obviously, means a tremendous step forward.

"Normal" Stars and Less Common Types

Our two diagrams were fortunate examples. Taken together, they yield much the same picture we would obtain by grouping all the stars whose absolute brightness has in some way become known.

According to present theories, the red giants and the stars of the main series (joined by an arrow in Figure 67) are considered "normal." The stars of the dwarf branch (that is, of the main series proper) probably have at their center a temperature of roughly 36 million degrees, while the surface temperature of the stars from A down to M ranges from 25,000° down to 3500°. Theoretically, the red giants are likely to have a lower temperature at the center, roughly 9 million degrees. The density of the red giants is slight, and increases steadily as we follow the arrow through our diagram. Stars that do not fit into this normal series must in some way be different. We are not yet sure of the reason for their deviation from the norm. Presumably, it is to be sought in their "chemical composition."

In recent years the concept of the "age" of stars has become more and more important. In diagrams of the sort we have dealt with in the last few pages, the "age" of the stars must be taken into consideration as a new unknown.

The Big Question: What Is the Source of the Energy That Radiates from the Stars?

Despite our elaborate statistical tables and theoretical deductions, we still do not know much about the stars. The most important questions remain quite without answers. What is the source of the energy that continuously pours out through the star's surface? It must be "liberated" somewhere within the star, somewhere in the innermost regions where conditions are least like those with which we are familiar.

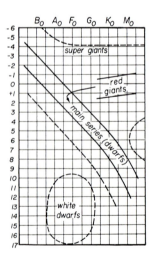

FIG. 67. Spectrum and luminosity: all the stars.

The key to an understanding of this production of energy lies in the processes taking place in the atomic nuclei. Astronomers and physicists have shown equal zeal in applying the findings of modern nuclear physics to this problem.

A star that shrinks from a large tenuous sphere of gas into a smaller, compact one, releases energy. Gas atoms fall toward the center, much as the water of a waterfall. Just as the waterfall can produce electric current, a star in the process of condensation can release a great amount of energy, which pours forth as radiation. But when we reckon how much energy our sun has released in shrinking to its present size, we are forced to conclude that this process can have provided radiation only for some 20 million years. Our sun cannot be so young. It must have radiated long before the crust of our earth began to form, that is at least 2 billion or a hundred times as many years ago. Shrinkage, though it certainly occurs, is not alone sufficient.

In the nuclei of the atoms, hydrogen nuclei are welded together into an almost indestructible whole. But where this nuclear complex disintegrates or is forced apart (atom splitting), well-nigh inexhaustible quantities of energy are released. This is what happens in the disintegration of radium and other radioactive elements. The released energy clings to the castoff helium nuclei and electrons, which fly off at tremendous speed. Their impact can produce considerable effects. However, the radioactive elements are in all probability not plentiful enough in the stars to contribute much to their radiation. A more plausible source of energy is the reverse process, the transformation of lighter atoms into heavier ones. For example, when four hydrogen nuclei join to form a helium nucleus, there occurs not just a simple moving-together but a complete regrouping of all parts and energies. Two of the four hydrogen electrons are

worked into the new helium nucleus, which in all probability can never again be torn apart. In this process
(which also plays a part in the hydrogen bomb) a vast
amount of energy must be released, for the helium
nucleus weighs appreciably less than the four hydrogen
nuclei that have gone into it.

There are sure to be still richer sources of energy, but
it is doubtful that they are now at work in the stars, since
they would require much higher temperatures and pressures. What we have in mind is the transformation of
particles of matter into radiation and vice versa, which
has been deduced from the theory of relativity and verified by the observation of cosmic rays.

There Is More to Be Learned from the Spectrum

It is time to recall what has drawn us into these deep
astrophysical problems: the lines in the star spectra,
which told us so many things after we once learned to
understand, at least in part, this language of light. Perhaps there is more to be learned.

Let us look at the spectra in Figure 68. In the lower
spectrum, all the dark lines are double. If we photograph
this star (Zeta in the Big Dipper, or Mizar) every five
nights, through a spectroscope, we find that within 20
days the K line will appear twice single and twice double. The process that is revealed by the duplication of
lines is periodic. Figure 69 will serve to explain it. We are
dealing here with a binary system whose two stars are

FIG. 68. Duplication in the spectral lines of
a double star (from photographs taken at
the Yerkes Observatory).

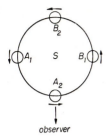

FIG. 69. Motions in a binary system.

observer

so close together that we cannot separate them in our telescope. The images of both stars fall simultaneously on the slit in the spectrograph, and we always obtain both spectra at once. In the case of Zeta Ursae Majoris, both stars are of the same spectral type, so that their spectra seem to be one. But from time to time two spectra appear. This occurs when the two stars stand at A_1 and B_1.

It would be a mistake to assume that the spectra appear side by side at this time because the stars are at their greatest distance from each other. The spectral line is after all an image of the slit, it is present whenever light falls on the slit, but it always remains in the same place, determined by the wave length of the light producing the image. The lines that appear side by side must therefore be produced by a somewhat different light, although the radiation is that of like atoms. The difference stems from the motion of the two sources of light: at A_1, star A is moving toward us, at B_1 star B is moving away from us. For the sake of a simple explanation, let us for the moment pretend that we can hear light.

Motion Changes the "Pitch"

We are in a railway station. A locomotive is waiting at a distance. We see by a white puff of steam that the locomotive is whistling, and a moment later we hear the whistling. The pitch of the whistle is determined by the

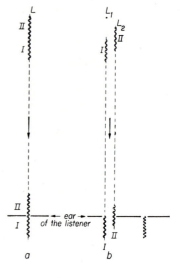

FIG. 70. Change of pitch caused by motion of the source of sound.

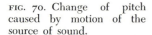

number of air vibrations per second that reach our ear. As long as the locomotive is standing still, the number of vibrations reaching our ear is the same as that sent out by the whistle. In Figure 70 (a) the wavy line starting at *L* indicates the stream of sound waves leaving the whistle in two seconds (there are several hundred vibrations). After a while this stream of waves, traveling at 1080 feet per second, reaches our ear. The figure shows the moment when the stream of waves emitted in the first second has entered our ear; that waves emitted in the next second are on the way.

Now suppose that at the end of the first second the locomotive suddenly leaps forward toward us (*b* in Figure 70). The second stream of waves now has a shorter distance to travel in order to reach us. Its beginning arrives before the end of the first stream. The same holds true if the locomotive, instead of starting forward, moves steadily toward us. In the course of a second, not only the stream of waves emitted in the first second, but a part of that emitted in the next second, enters the ear. The ear registers more vibrations than before and hears a somewhat higher tone. When the locomotive moves away, the tone is lower. The faster the locomotive travels, the greater the change in pitch, and the easier it is to observe. If we stand by the railway tracks and a train happens to pass by at 50 miles an hour, blowing its whistle, we do not need a fine ear to observe that at the moment it passes us the pitch of the whistle drops suddenly by a whole tone. A horn of a passing auto or siren of a passing police car teaches the same lesson.

Exactly the same thing happens with light—though we shall leave it to the physicists to prove it. And herein lies the explanation of our variable double star spectrum: we see the light of the star that is coming toward us somewhat "higher" (more violet), that of the star moving away from us a little "lower" (redder), than at position A_2B_2, where both stars are moving at a right angle to our line of sight so that for some time there is no change in their distance from us. In the continuous spectrum, the change in the pitch of light cannot be observed because every strip of spectrum that moves a bit toward the violet is at once replaced by the adjacent redder strip which in its new place has the same color as the one that went before. But where there is a bright or a dark line (corresponding to a tone), we see it shift toward the violet or the red.

We must, of course, take care to obtain a very clear spectrum for these observations, and if we wish not merely to see but to make measurements we must use instruments that enable us to draw the spectrum apart. In general we are dealing with only very slight shifts in our lines. For the lines of a double star to be as far apart as the two yellow sodium lines, the two stars must travel at a velocity of roughly 100 miles per second, one

Zeiss three-prism spectrograph

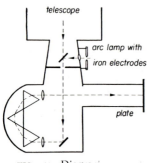

FIG. 71. Diagram.

FIG. 72. Attached to the large re-fractor of the Hamburg Observatory.

toward us, the other away from us. Although such veloci-ties occur most double stars move much more slowly.

Double Stars That Are Never Seen Double

Only relatively few spectroscopic binaries can show the lines of both stars in the spectrum; most often one of the two stars is so much fainter than the other that its lines do not appear at all. There is then no splitting of lines, but only an oscillation of the one line system. How can this be seen, when all the lines oscillate evenly, so that the general image remains the same? In these cases we need another spectrum for comparison, to show the normal position of the lines.

We customarily use an iron spectrum whose many lines supply a good basis for comparison. The iron spectrum is produced by electrical vaporization, for example in an arc lamp with iron electrodes. The light from the incan-descent iron vapor is cast into the telescope from the side, where a mirror directs it into the slit of the spectro-graph (Figs. 71 and 72). One iron spectrum is taken before the celestial photograph, another after it, to make sure that no change has occurred in the spectrograph itself. Screens are so placed that the starlight falls only on the middle of the slit, the artificial light only on the upper and lower ends.

The result is shown in Figure 73. In both photographs, the black bands with bright lines are iron spectra, the broad spectra with dark lines are those of a double star at different times. Lines of the star spectrum that coincide with the iron lines show that in both cases the star lines are shifted to the right—below twice as much as above. The velocities corresponding to these shifts are 24 and 45 miles a second.

Among the bright stars alone that can be so investigated, more than 1000 double stars have been found. Of the stars of spectral class B, probably more than half are binaries. To us dwellers on a satellite of a simple sun this observation is surprising, and worth knowing for its own sake. But we also learn something else for our pains.

We are here measuring the true velocity of stars, in miles a second, and not only their apparent velocity as we did with the visual binaries (p. 55). Consequently, the determination of their orbits tells us the real distance

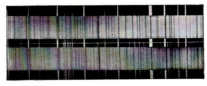

FIG. 73. Two photographs of the same star on different days. Dark lines: star spectrum; bright lines: iron comparison spectrum (from photographs of the Yerkes Observatory).

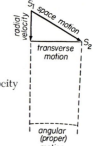

FIG. 74. Space motion derived from radial velocity and transverse motion.

between them, so that we can form a concrete picture of the system. It would be most desirable to learn something about their mass as well, since we have no direct way of measuring the mass of single stars. But our spectrographic methods do not give us the distance and mass of double stars. We get complete data only if the system also can be observed as a visual binary, or if it is an eclipsing variable.

Radial Velocity, Proper Motion, Real Motion

It is not only in double stars that we find displacement of lines. None of the "fixed" stars is fixed. Each one is engaged in a long journey, and the displacement of its spectrum shows how much closer or farther away from the earth it moves per second. This part of its motion we call radial velocity.

That part of the star's motion which is perpendicular to our line of sight may with patience be observed as a movement in the sky (Fig. 74); the angle between the two rays striking the observer (which is in fact much more acute than shown in the diagram) determines the star's proper motion (p. 38). Only if the distance of the star is known can we tell how large its real transverse motion is. But in that case, we can also determine the star's true motion S_1S_2 from its radial velocity and transverse motion. The real motion, as the figure shows, is the third side of a right triangle. It would be very helpful if we could make these computations for a great many stars. But we know only the distances of the close stars with sufficient accuracy. The radial velocities, however, give us roughly the same information of the rate of motion, and for the more distant stars that is all we can get.

The table below shows the velocities of the brightest stars.

Radial Velocities of the Brightest Stars

| STAR | SPECTRUM | POSITION | | RADIAL VELOCITY |
		R.A.	DECL.	MILE/SEC.
Achernar	B5	1^h 36^m	−57°	+12
Aldebaran	K5	4 33	+16	+33
Capella	Go	5 13	+46	+18
Rigel	B8	5 12	−8	+15
Betelgeuse	Mo	5 52	+7	+13
Canopus	Fo	6 23	−53	+12
Sirius	Ao	6 43	−17	−4
Procyon	F5	7 37	+5	−2
Pollux	Ko	7 42	+28	+2
Regulus	B8	10 6	+12	+2
Beta Crucis	B1	12 45	−59	+12
Spica	B2	13 23	−11	+1
Beta Centauri	B1	14 0	−60	−7
Arcturus	Ko	14 13	+19	−3
Alpha Centauri	Go	14 36	−61	-14
Antares	Mo	16 26	−26	−2
Vega	Ao	18 35	+39	−9
Altair	A5	19 48	+9	−16
Deneb	A2	20 40	+45	−4
Fomalhaut	A3	22 55	−30	+4

A study of these radical velocities yields the surprising fact that almost the entire first half of the stars are moving away from us, while almost all the others are moving toward us. A glance at their positions shows that the approaching stars are in one-half of the sky, the other stars in the other half. Their motion reflects our own motion, the motion of the solar system. It is we who are moving toward the point in the sky at 18 o'clock and +30°, we who are moving away from the opposite point at six o'clock and —30°, at a rate of 12 miles a second.

We measure from the earth, and thus obtain different radial velocities at different seasons—for the motion of the spectrum lines expresses the motion of the source of light, and of the observer, relative to one another. The additional velocity, which is caused by the earth's own motion and which we can compute on the basis of our very exact knowledge of the earth's orbit, must also be deducted. The radial velocities in the table above have been corrected so as to be "relative to the sun."

Slow and Fast Stars

We can next deduct the effects of the sun's motion. What remains expresses the velocities of stars themselves. But we must bear in mind that although we have determined the radial velocities of some 7000 stars, we know the true direction of only a few of them. Only for these last can we compute true velocity. We can measure the full velocity of stars moving along our line of sight; for those stars that are moving crosswise, we can measure no velocity at all: on an average, then, we can measure the real motions of only half the stars. The following table shows the average velocities at which the stars move through space:

| SPECTRAL TYPE | VELOCITY IN SPACE | |
	MAIN SERIES (DWARFS)	GIANTS
B	12 mile/sec.	
A	16	
F	23	20 mile/sec.
G	42	21
K	39	25
M	45	26

The sun, we see, is among the slow-moving stars in its class (G dwarfs). Velocities much greater than these averages are rare. But we also know of "racers" that cover more than 60 miles a second; a good part of the faint dwarf stars seem to be of this type (p. 175).

Movements in and on the Stars

It is in some ways a good thing that we see the stars at great distances, so that our spectroscopic observation deals only with the total radiation of the stars as a whole. But it is also a good thing that we can observe at least one star—the sun—from close by.

The sun allows us to examine the "surface" of a ball of gas and to ascertain that it is definitely not a rigid mass (Fig. 75). The spectroscope shows gases streaming

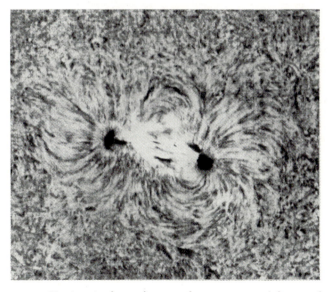

FIG. 75. Vortices in the sun's atmosphere: sunspots (photograph of the Mount Wilson Observatory, taken in red hydrogen light).

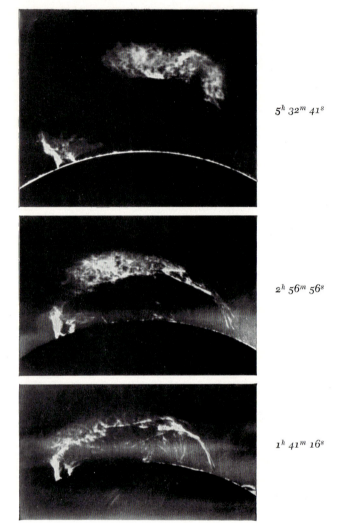

$5^h\ 32^m\ 41^s$

$2^h\ 56^m\ 56^s$

$1^h\ 41^m\ 16^s$

FIG. 76. Large prominence on May 29, 1919 (photograph of the Mount Wilson Observatory, taken in violet calcium light).

FIG. 77. The outermost atmosphere of the sun, the "corona," which becomes visible in a total eclipse of the sun when the moon shuts out the bright light of the solar disk. (June 29, 1927: expedition of the Hamburg Observatory to Jokkmokk in Lapland.)

upward and downward in the sun's atmosphere at velocities of several miles a second. But there also occur eruptions of gas (prominences, Figure 76), shooting up at velocities of several hundred miles a second to heights of up to 60,000 miles. We can observe these phenomena only on the sun, but we are convinced that they occur in all the stars.

In special cases the line spectrum tells us something about movements in the atmosphere even of distant stars, as in the case of the novae (p. 87). The dark (absorption) lines in their spectra are greatly displaced toward the violet, indicating that, in the gas cover in which the star is wrapped, matter is moving swiftly toward us, or, generally speaking, is moving outward. This motion attains velocities of several hundred miles a second, and in the course of half a year produces an expansion of the star's gas envelope up to the size of our whole solar system. This large and very tenuous gas cover makes itself known also by bright, only slightly displaced lines (Fig. 78) which stem from the sides of the envelope, while the dark lines come from the small central zone through which we look at the star's continuously radiating photosphere (Fig. 79).

After a while, the radiation of the gas envelope wholly submerges the continuous radiation of the photosphere (Fig. 78, bottom). The radiation of the gas envelope, at first much inflated, now gradually shrinks. In the end— as it would appear from our observations so far—we find a very much smaller and hence much more densely

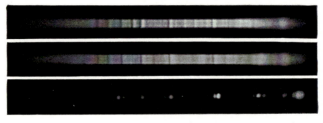

FIG. 78. Spectra of the Nova Herculis in January, March, and September, 1935 (Lippert astrograph of the Hamburg Observatory).

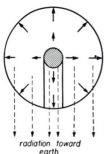

radiation toward earth

FIG. 79. Movements in the atmosphere of a nova.

packed star, surrounded by an envelope of tenuous matter which seems somehow to have become superfluous and is moving outward.

Double stars that are very close together have yielded interesting information about the nature of star atmospheres. When the two stars of one of these systems are in a favorable position, streams of gas between them may be seen from the spectrum lines. Some of the swiftly rotating O and B stars (see p. 85) are probably surrounded by a ring of gas. The centrifugal force has grown so great that the star can no longer hold all its gases to its surface.

In our enthusiasm we may have said a little more than can be proved by observation alone. But such speculative enthusiasm is absolutely indispensable to the advance of scientific inquiry. As we look back over the paths of knowledge that have been opened by spectrum analysis, our enthusiasm has justified itself.

PART TWO: *The World of the Stars*

I. OUR ISLAND IN THE UNIVERSE

Some astronomers spend their whole lives with a meridian circle, measuring star positions; others do nothing but determine radial velocities. It is even possible that an astronomer who has been tripped up in his search for the secrets of the heavens by inadequate methods and instruments will have to give the rest of his days to improving the unsatisfactory tools, without, in a manner of speaking, ever seeing the sky again. There is a tendency to smile at such men as eccentrics, or pity them as poor victims. Both views are wrong. In the far-flung enterprise of scientific research, the specialization of these men is just as necessary as is that in economic life. Science needs no more than a few great intellects who draw the facts of observation together into an over-all picture and, with the vision of great minds, complete the picture beyond the limits of what is known. But it needs a great many skilled, hard-working laborers to amass the material that proves or disproves such theories and contains the germs of new "visions." Our discussions show, I trust, that such day-to-day work is by no means tedious, arduous though it may be. They may also alert us to the danger of becoming so immersed in specialized efforts that we lose sight of the main goal!

A Model of the Universe

We, too, set ourselves a goal: to build a model of the universe, where everything that we see in the sky would have its place. Now that we have amassed such an abundance of knowledge about the stars, what progress have we made?

Let us begin by building a model in the literal sense. Our own position—the sun, or the whole solar system— from which we look at the universe will be a small wooden ball into which we can stick knitting needles. At first, we limit ourselves to our "immediate" vicinity and represent only objects that are no more than 16 light-years away (table, p. 144). Here we need only 53 knitting needles. The directions in which they point are given by the star positions; and the length at which we must snip them off and put a head on them to represent each star is indicated by the star's distance—provided we have first established the scale of our model.

In order that our universe may not be too cumbersome, let us give it a diameter of 12 inches. Our longest needles, representing the stars 16 light-years away, will then be 6 inches long; the shortest needles will be those of the double star Alpha Centauri, and of Proxima Centauri (*proxima* = nearest); Sirius will be roughly 3½ inches from the center of the model. To make it true to life, we should make the stars shine. Sirius should shine roughly a million times as bright as the faintest stars in the table, and they should shine in different colors. This could be done with light bulbs. But we shall run into difficulties if we attempt to give the bulbs the size proportionate to scale. The sun in our model should have a diameter of only .00000003 inches, and even the largest stars should be at most a hundred times larger. We shall have to dispense with this degree of accuracy, and make do with pinheads, which are much larger than scale size. Even so, our model gives a good picture of our immediate vicinity in space.

We may want to add a few stars of which we do not yet know that they are in our immediate vicinity. The 53

STAR		POSITION		
		RIGHT ASCENSION	DECLI- NATION	DISTANCE (LIGHT-YEARS)
Sun		...	...	...
1. Alpha Centauri	A	} 14ʰ 36ᵐ	−60.6	}
2.	B			
3. (Proxima Centauri)	C	14 27	−62.5	} 4
4. Barnard's star	⁕	17 55	+4.5	6
5. Wolf 359		10 54	+7.3	8
6. Luyten 726–8	A	} 1 36	−18.2	} 8
7.	B			
8. Lalande 21185	⁕	11 1	+36.3	8
9. Sirius	A	} 6 43	−16.6	} 9
10.	B			
11. Ross 154		18 47	−23.9	9
12. Ross 248		23 39	+43.9	10
13. Epsilon Eridani		3 31	−9.6	11
14. Ross 128		11 45	+1.1	11
15. 61 Cygni	A⁕	} 21 5	+38.5	} 11
16.	B			
17. Luyten 789–6		22 36	−15.6	11
18. Procyon	A	} 7 37	+5.3	} 11
19.	B			
20. Epsilon Indi		22 0	−57.0	11
21. BD +59° 1915	A	} 18 42	+59.5	} 12
22.	B			
23. BD +43° 44	A	} 0 15	+43.7	} 12
24.	B			
25. Tau Ceti		1 42	−16.2	12
26. CD −36° 15693		23 3	−36.1	12
27. BD +5° 1668		7 25	+5.5	12
28. CD −39° 14192		21 14	−39.1	13
29. CD −45° 1841		5 10	−45.0	13
30. BD +56° 2783	A	} 22 26	+57.4	} 13
31.	B			
32. Ross 614		6 27	−7.8	13
33. BD −12° 4523		16 27	−12.5	13
34. Wolf 28		0 46	+5.2	14
35. Wolf 424	A	} 12 31	+9.3	} 15
36.	B			
37. BD +50° 1725		10 8	+49.7	15
38. CD −37° 15492		0 2	−37.6	15
39. CD −46° 11540		17 25	+46.8	15
40. BD +20° 2465	⁕	10 17	+20.1	15
41. CD −44° 11909		17 33	−44.3	15
42. CD −49° 13515		21 30	−49.2	16
43. BD +68° 946		17 37	+68.4	16
44. Ross 780		22 50	−14.5	16
45. Lalande 25372		13 43	+15.2	16
46. CC 658		11 43	−64.5	16
47. 40 Eridani	A	}		}
48.	B	} 4 13	−7.7	} 16
49.	C			
50. 70 Ophiuchi	A	} 18 3	+2.5	} 16
51.	B			
52. Altair		19 48	+8.7	16
53. BD +43° 4305		22 45	+44.1	16

⁕ This star has an invisible companion with a mass between that
† Light-years in units of 10,000 years: + = away from us, − =

ABSOLUTE BRIGHTNESS (MAGNITUDE)	LUMINOSITY (× SUN)	SPECTRAL TYPE	MOTION † RADIAL	TRANVERSE
4.7	1.0	Go	...	...
4.7	1.0	Go ⎫		
6.1	0.28	K5 ⎬ −0.8		0.8
15.4	0.00005	M5 ⎭		
13.2	0.0004	M5	−3.6	3.0
16.6	0.00002	M6	+0.4	1.8
15.6	0.00004	M6 ⎰ +1.0		1.3
16.1	0.00003	M6 ⎱		
10.5	0.005	M2	−2.9	1.9
1.3	23	Ao ⎰ −0.3		0.6
10.0	0.004	w.d. ⎱		
13.3	0.0004	M5	−0.1	0.3
14.7	0.0001	M6	−2.7	0.8
6.2	0.25	K2	+0.5	0.5
13.5	0.0003	M5	−0.4	0.7
7.9	0.05	K6 ⎰ −2.1		2.8
8.6	0.03	Mo ⎱		
14.5	0.0001	M6	−2.0	1.8
2.8	6	F5 ⎰ −0.1		0.7
13.1	0.0004	w.d. ⎱		
7.0	0.1	K5	−1.4	2.6
11.1	0.003	M4 ⎰ 0.0		1.3
11.9	0.001	M4 ⎱		
10.3	0.006	M2 ⎰ +0.5		1.6
13.1	0.0004	M4 ⎱		
5.8	0.4	G4	−0.5	1.1
9.4	0.01	M2	+0.3	3.9
12.2	0.001	M4	+0.9	2.2
8.6	0.03	M1	+0.8	2.1
11.2	0.002	Mo	+8.1	5.5
11.9	0.001	M4 ⎰ −0.8		0.5
13.4	0.0003	M5 ⎱		
12.9	0.0005	M5	+0.8	0.6
11.9	0.001	M5	−0.4	0.8
14.2	0.0002	w.d.(F)	+0.9	2.0
14.3	0.0001	M6 ⎰ −0.2		1.3
14.3	0.0001	M6 ⎱		
8.5	0.03	K5	−0.9	1.0
10.3	0.006	M3	+0.8	4.4
11.3	0.002	M4	?	0.8
11.1	0.003	M4	+0.3	0.4
12.8	0.0006	M5	?	0.9
10.6	0.004	M3	?	0.6
10.7	0.004	M3	−0.6	1.0
11.8	0.001	M5	+0.3	0.9
10.2	0.006	M2	+0.5	1.8
12.5	0.001	w.d.	?	2.1
6.0	0.3	Ko ⎫		
10.7	0.004	w.d.(A) ⎬ −1.4		3.2
12.5	0.001	M5 ⎭		
5.7	0.3	K1 ⎰ −0.2		0.9
7.4	0.1	K5 ⎱		
2.4	8	A5	−0.9	0.5
11.7	0.002	M5	−0.1	0.7

of a planet and that of a normal star. w.d. = white dwarf.
toward us.

stars in our table are stars whose distances have been measured, and for a good reason. Some of them were studied because they are bright stars; others were companions of bright stars; still others, by their large proper motion, led astronomers to suspect that they were close. And since we are far from having picked out of the multitude of faint stars all those with large proper motions, it is quite possible that there are still another 5, or 10, or 15 stars that actually ought to be in our model.

Still more stars will be missing if we double our diameter, to include those 250 odd-stars that are no more than 32 light-years away, for there may be stars at the outer edge of this new sphere that are not bright enough for us to see. (There are also stars that are quite dark!) If we finally extend our model to a diameter of 10 feet, we can place in it the 2000 stars whose trigonometric parallaxes are known—and yet we must admit that it is not a model of the real universe. Now it is a thousand times as large as our first model with its 53 stars, and still it contains not even one hundred times as many stars. If we had not studied how distances are determined, the sight of this model would convince us that the density of stars decreases sharply as we move outward, and that beyond this 9-foot ball the universe soon stops entirely. But the limit we have reached is the limit, not of the universe, but only of our powers of observation. We see an abundance of stars—5000 with the naked eye alone, and the "Bonn Survey" of the northern sky, even though it was prepared with a very small telescope, contains all of 300,000 stars. The trouble is that we cannot find out which ones belong within the area of our model.

A Sally into the Distance

We know that we cannot penetrate this outer cosmos with our usual methods of distance measurement (p. 49). But we recall another way of arriving at the distance of a star (p. 82). We need to know its apparent and its absolute brightness; from these two, the distance can be derived by a very simple computation (photometric parallaxes). The table on page 83 saves us even this effort. For example, we have observed that a star with the apparent magnitude $M = 13$ has the absolute magnitude $M = 12$, the value of $m - M = 11$ (in the first column) gives us its distance of 5200 light-years (in the second). The apparent brightness we can measure, but the absolute brightness we must seek to obtain somehow. Certain peculiarities of the spectrum provide the means (spectroscopic parallaxes, p. 125). The accuracy of this method at the 150-light-year limit is today much higher than that of the trigonometric method; and its importance lies precisely in this unchanging reliability even at great distances. Again, there is a limit: we need good spectra, which means that the stars must not be too faint. We may in the foreseeable future expect to have spectroscopic distance determinations for the 100,000-odd stars down to the ninth magnitude. Among the stars of the twelfth magnitude, whose distance has been measured with lesser accuracy, there are some extremely luminous stars that are as much as 10,000 light-years distant; but it does not seem likely that the distances of all stars of the twelfth magnitude (more than one million of them) will ever be computed.

Here again we reach a limit; it is impossible to investigate every single one of the vast multitude of stars. A few thousand stars we get to know "personally"; all the others remain "stars," which we can count and classify according to various characteristics (position, brightness, color, spectrum) without attempting to observe everything that distinguishes each from all others (distance, mass, volume, luminosity). We must accept such limits to our observation though we do not mean to abandon our efforts to penetrate the "chaos" of the outer world.

An Indirect Approach

We can always count the stars. The brighter stars have been so counted; down to about the ninth magnitude. They are fully listed in the surveys and, down to the eleventh or twelfth magnitude, in the catalogues of the "Photographic Star Chart." To count all the millions of faint stars in the photographs taken with the large telescopes we would need a great deal of time, and it is not necessary. When dealing with such multitudes of stars, we are content with samples.

Instead of investigating the entire sky, we select certain fields so distributed that we are sure to have a sampling of the most diverse parts of the sky (for instance, of the Milky Way). For convenience, we choose a telescope marking exactly one square degree on the photographic plate—a square of sky in which four full moons would fit. With this telescope we prepare exposures of different lengths. First, we expose the plate just long enough so that stars of the eighth magnitude, but no fainter ones, will show up. Next, we expose the plate 3 times as long, to show stars of the ninth magnitude—and so on down to the twenty-first magnitude. When we have counted all the stars on these plates we know how many stars up to a given magnitude we see in our field. We do not always get the same results; neighboring fields may differ—one field may contain two or three bright stars, and the neighboring field none. To reduce such differences, we combine the figures for similar fields into averages. In the compilation below, Column I refers to fields in the Milky Way and its immediate vicinity; Column II to fields far removed from it.

Even in Column I the figures are much larger than we should have expected: almost 100,000 stars to one degree square. And from the way the figures mount we may be sure that we should have twice as many if we could go a few magnitudes lower. It is precisely these vast multitudes of faint stars that produce the milky shimmer of the Milky Way.

Can we draw any live conclusions from these dry figures? For a start, let us make things a good deal simpler than they are. Let us assume that all stars have the same absolute brightness, the same luminosity. In that case, only their varying distance accounts for their varying brightness, that is, their apparent brightness indicates their distance: the stars of sixth magnitude are a little more than $1\frac{1}{2}$ times as far away as those of the fifth magnitude (see the table on p. 83). The stars of the seventh magnitude are a little more than $1\frac{1}{2}$ times as far away as those of the 6th and so on.

LIMITING MAGNITUDE	NUMBER OF STARS PER SQUARE DEGREE	
	I	II
8	1	...
9	3	...
10	8	1–2
11	21	4–5
12	55	10
13	145	21
14	370	45
15	910	87
16	2140	160
17	4800	290
18	10,200	480
19	21,000	760
20	40,000	1180
21	74,000	1660

The zone of space we are examining when we count over a field of one square degree is a pyramid with its tip in our eye; no matter where we cut it off (at stars with an apparent brightness of 1.0, 2.0, . . . 21.0), it has a square base. This base grows larger and larger the farther out we look. When we cut off the pyramid at twice the distance, the base is four times as large; the volume of the pyramid becomes 8 times as large, and with it grows the number of the stars contained in it, assuming them to be evenly distributed. The intervals between our cut-off points (based on magnitudes) are somewhat shorter; each cut-off is roughly 1½ times as far as the preceding one. Accordingly, whenever we extend our counting of stars by one magnitude, we may expect the number of stars to be almost 4 times as large as before. But this holds only if the concentration of stars is everywhere the same, that is, if equal zones of space contain everywhere equal numbers of stars. If at greater distances the stars are less plentiful, our count will increase more slowly; and when we enter into a region with a greater concentration of stars, we shall meet more than fourfold increases.

It looks as though such star counts might teach us something about the structure of our universe. In our compilation on page 149, the relation of successive figures is never 4 : 1, but always smaller. This means that every new segment of the pyramid adds fewer stars than it would if the star concentration were uniform—in other words, that star concentration decreases as we move outward. Outside the Milky Way (Column II), star concentration obviously decreases much more quickly. It looks as if we were approaching a limit beyond which no new stars would be added to our figures. That, then, would be the limit of our stellar system.

Let us quickly recall that our nice, simple conclusions rest on the totally false assumption that all stars have the same absolute brightness. How mistaken it is one glance at Figure 67 will show. But it will also show that our assumption is nearly correct if, instead of counting all the stars together, we take each spectral class by itself.

For the very faint stars we cannot do so, because when we spread out their light into a spectrum no light is left. Unfortunately, Figure 67 also shows us that the red stars (classes K and M) include two kinds. Even if there were stars of only two absolute brightnesses, say, 5.0 and 15.0, matters would be much more involved. At a distance of $32\frac{1}{2}$ light-years, the less luminous stars would have an apparent brightness of 15.0 (p. 83); at a distance of $3\frac{1}{4}$ light-years they would appear as stars of magnitude 10.0. It is unlikely that there are any stars closer to us. Hence, so long as our count does not include the tenth magnitude, we cannot have counted any of the less luminous stars. The number of stars counted up to that point has quadrupled with each magnitude, and continues to grow at that rate. But from the tenth magnitude on, the less luminous stars enter. At this point, there should be a big jump in the figures.

As we know, the facts are much more complex. Within certain limits, there are stars of every conceivable luminosity. Our simple example, however, leads us to believe that even though reality is more complex, it will be possible to establish a relation between the figures arrived at by sorting and counting and the frequency of stars in different regions of space. With mathematics and with patience, the problem can be solved. We are compelled to assume that in the regions in which we do our counting the stars of different absolute brightness are mixed in the same proportions as in our immediate vicinity, where the proportions of the mixture can be established. According to our experience up to now, this assumption seems justified; but we must be prepared for the possibility that somewhere—and perhaps precisely in the outer parts of the stellar system—these proportions will be different.

The Great Obstacle: The Absorption of Light in Space

Our calculations imply another assumption that we have thus far taken for granted. In comparing apparent with absolute brightness, we have assumed that the light impression made by a star becomes fainter with increasing distance only because the light is spread over a steadily increasing area. But it may also be that light is absorbed in cosmic space. Of two stars equally luminous, the one that is twice as far away would then actually send less than one-quarter as much light into our telescope as the other—how much less will depend on how much of its radiation is absorbed and scattered.

If there is such a universal absorption, we see all the stars as fainter than they would appear otherwise; in other words, our calculations up to now have assigned to them excessive distances, and the farther away they are, the greater our error. Of course we can compute the extent of these mistakes—if they are mistakes. By way of an example, let us assume that cosmic absorption reduces the light of a star by one-sixth (or one-third) of a magnitude for every 1000 light-years' distance. A star 3000 light-years away will then appear half a magnitude (or a whole magnitude) fainter than it would without absorption; one that is 30,000 light-years away will appear 5 (or 10) magnitudes fainter. What we have computed in both cases instead of the correct distance r_0 is shown by Columns r_1 and r_2 in the following table.

From these figures we see to our dismay that absorption is negligible only for the smallest distances, but it distorts larger distances to such an extent as to give us an entirely false view of the universe. Perhaps there is no such falling-off of star concentration as we have concluded from the figures on page 149; perhaps we have drawn this conclusion only because we have distributed

| CORRECT | FALSE DISTANCE | | DIMINUTION OF |
| r_0 | r_1 | r_2 | BRIGHTNESS IN |
(LIGHT-YEARS)	(LIGHT-YEARS)	(LIGHT-YEARS)	MAGNITUDES
10	10	10	$\frac{1}{600}$ $\frac{1}{300}$
100	101	102	$\frac{1}{60}$ $\frac{1}{30}$
500	520	540	$\frac{1}{12}$ $\frac{1}{6}$
1000	1080	1170	$\frac{1}{6}$ $\frac{1}{3}$
2000	2330	2720	$\frac{1}{3}$ $\frac{2}{3}$
3000	3780	4750	$\frac{1}{2}$ 1
4000	5440	7390	$\frac{2}{3}$ $1\frac{1}{3}$
5000	7340	10,800	$\frac{5}{6}$ $1\frac{2}{3}$
10,000	21,500	46,400	$1\frac{2}{3}$ $3\frac{1}{3}$
20,000	93,000	431,000	$3\frac{1}{3}$ $6\frac{2}{3}$
30,000	300,000	3,000,000	5 10
40,000	860,000	19,000,000	$6\frac{2}{3}$ $13\frac{1}{3}$
50,000	2,300,000	108,000,000	$8\frac{1}{3}$ $16\frac{2}{3}$

each new series of stars over far too great a space. If we disregard absorption, we arrive at the conception of a limited stellar system, settled more and more thinly as we move outward. But if we assume that absorption occurs, the same data mean that we are situated somewhere in an unfathomable sea of stars.

Dust Clouds in the Stellar System

In consequence, we simply must look into this phenomenon of absorption. That there is such a thing cannot be doubted. Let us take a look at a number of photographs of the Milky Way (Figs. 11 and 80). What is the meaning of the "dark" regions that show few stars, of the stripes, the canals, the dark holes? It is possible, of course, that the star clouds we see as the Milky Way are placed here in such a way that we can see through them into empty and consequently dark space. But considering that we are peering through distances of some thousands of light-years, it seems unlikely that in so many places our line of sight should pass uninterrupted between star clouds. It seems far more plausible that in these directions there is something in the way, something that obstructs our view of distant star clouds.

There are numerous bright nebulae (Figs. 11, 80, 81), and since we know that they are luminous only because they are lit up by stars in their vicinity, we may be sure that there are other dark nebulae which we notice only where they hide certain fields of regions rich in stars. If there is a very dense or thick cloud in such regions, we see only the stars that lie in front of it; if the cloud does not absorb all the light of the stars behind it, at least it causes them to appear fainter, so that the number of stars below a certain determinable apparent brightness appears smaller than in the unobscured vicinity. In such

FIG. 80. Milky Way in Ophiuchus (Bruce refractor of the Yerkes Observatory).

FIG. 81. Nebula in Cygnus (14-inch Schmidt telescope of the Hamburg Observatory).

cases we can deduce from star counts at what distances the cloud begins and ends. The cloud in Cygnus, for example (Figs. 83 and 84), is 1500 light-years away and has a depth of 500 light-years. It is hard to form an exact notion of such cosmic clouds. They are certainly much thinner than our earthly mists or clouds, much thinner even than our air itself. They must for the most part consist not of gases (because gases do not absorb enough) but of some sort of "dust."

Not only are separate clouds of this sort present between stars; the whole stellar system is filled with highly attenuated gas and fine dust. The mass of this "inter-

FIG. 82. Cave nebula in Cygnus (39-inch reflector of the Hamburg Observatory).

stellar matter" is so great, despite its extreme tenuousness, as to be comparable to the mass concentrated in the stars. Hence in studying the motions and forces in our stellar system we must take the matter between the stars into account.

The most important and simplest indication of the presence of matter between us and the stars is the discoloration of starlight. The light of the stars is not only weakened but reddened, since the blue light is more weakened than the red. Exactly the same thing holds true on earth. The sunlight is reddened as it passes through air: any sunset, when the light must travel a longer way through the earth's atmosphere, shows the result. If we did not remember the white noonday sun, the red sunset would probably not draw our attention.

To know whether a star is discolored, we first need to know its natural color. We can tell its natural color if we know its spectral type (p. 119), which we derive from

FIG. 83. Luminous edge of nebula in Cygnus. We see the right half of the field through a dust cloud. (39-inch reflector of the Hamburg Observatory.)

its line spectrum, independently of its seeming color. Each spectral type has a definite color, corresponding to the temperature of the star; and this color we designate by the color index, that is, by the difference between the star's brightness in blue and in yellow light (see the table on p. 121). Our sun, for example, has spectral type G_0, and thus in the table on page 121 the color index +0.6 magnitude. At sunset the brightness in blue light would be greatly obscured, so that we should have a considerably higher color index.

If we now take a faint G_0 star and measure a color index of +1.1 magnitudes, such as is normal for a K_0 star, its light is too red by 0.5 magnitude. This 0.5 magnitude is called color excess. It is a most important datum, because there is a fairly constant relation between total absorption of light and color excess. Hence, if we have measured a star's color excess as +0.5, the total light of

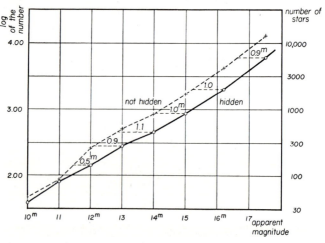

FIG. 84. Number of stars per square degree on the left and right sides of Figure 83. (The count includes all stars from the brightest to those of the seventeenth magnitude.)

this star is $5 \times 0.5 = 2.5$ magnitudes fainter than it would be without absorption by interstellar matter. Once we know this much, we can compute the star's corrected photometric distance.

Among the highly attenuated gases filling the space between the stars, calcium appears most clearly in the star spectra; it produces a fine absorption line, the so-called K line. This line occurs in star spectra even where there is no absorption, because calcium is present in the star atmospheres as it is in the atmosphere of the sun. Certain spectroscopic binaries exhibit a remarkable phenomenon: their spectrum includes sharp K lines that do not oscillate with the other lines (p. 128). These lines could not come from calcium atmospheres enveloping both stars together, because the sharp K lines appear in the spectra of stars that otherwise show only blurred lines. Sharp "interstellar" sodium lines have also been found. In general, the lines grow more pronounced as the stars grow more distant. This is in keeping with the notion that the longer the starlight travels through space the more calcium (or sodium) atoms it encounters. The intensity of this "motionless" calcium line has today become an approximate measure of star distances, particularly in the case of novae, which by reason of their great brightness can be observed even at great distances.

Computations show that on an average a cubic inch of interstellar space contains roughly 15 calcium atoms. By way of comparison, a similar volume of our air contains some 450 quintillion (45,000,000,000,000,000) molecules.

Another remarkable phenomenon has recently been discovered in the light of certain stars that has passed through large clouds. The light is slightly but distinctly "polarized." Light is an electromagnetic wave, whose vibrations run crosswise to its line of travel. This means that light coming toward us may vibrate from left to right, up and down, and in every direction between these.

In the natural light that comes from a star or say from an automobile headlight, all these vibrations occur equally. By means of special filters that are used in earthly photography—for instance in three-dimensional motion pictures—this or that direction of vibration can be suppressed. The remaining light we call "polarized." The same filters can also examine starlight for polarization. The reasons for polarization of starlight are still not clear. We assume that the cause lies in magnetically ordered metal crystals in space, which research has shown to have the power to polarize light.

Star Clusters

There are two very different kinds of star clusters. The so-called open clusters are groups of from a few dozen to a few thousand stars in totally irregular distribution (Fig. 85), star families with a common past and future of

FIG. 85. Two open star clusters in Perseus (Lippert astrograph of the Hamburg Observatory).

FIG. 86. Globular cluster in Serpens (39-inch reflector of the Hamburg Observatory).

their own, scattered about among the individual stars of our system. We know a good deal about their arrangement in space, because several of their stars (in the brighter and more populous clusters, many stars) can be used—again by means of spectral type and absolute brightness in conjunction with apparent brightness—to determine the distance of the whole cluster. The open clusters all lie in a flat, lens-shaped area with its greatest width in the plane of the Milky Way and a diameter of 30,000 light-years, while its thickness (perpendicular to the plane of the Milky Way) amounts to no more than 3000 light-years.

Globular clusters are quite different formations (Fig. 86). Innumerable stars are concentrated in a small circular spot. In many clusters they are truly innumerable, because they are so close together at the center that they cannot be seen separately. But we know that there are hundreds of thousands of them, sometimes millions. These clusters are complete star systems of a special kind, and they lie far outside the region in which we have moved so far.

Approximately 100 globular clusters are known. The nearest is 20,000 light-years distant, the farthest almost 200,000. These distances are so vast that we must once again consider the question how it is possible to determine them. When stars appear in such swarms, their spectra cannot be kept separate; we must look for other indications of absolute brightness. A method that is somewhat crude but quite effective for a start is to pick out the 25 brightest stars in the cluster, determine their average apparent brightness, and take for their absolute brightness the highest value encountered elsewhere.

The distance of clusters containing Cepheid variables (p. 79) can be established with much greater certainty. We know that the rapidly changing variables of this kind in the Magellanic Cloud (with periods of less than half a day) all have the same brightness—an absolute brightness of zero. Hence, if such stars in a cluster have apparent magnitude 18, then the cluster, according to our table of distances (p. 83), must be 130,000 light-years away. It may seem rather hazardous to assume that such stars will have the same absolute brightness wherever we encounter them. But since we are convinced that the quantity of light emitted and the way in which it changes are both determined by the star's physical state, we believe our conclusion to be legitimate.

The globular clusters also lie on both sides of the Milky Way and are somewhat more frequent closer to it. But within the Milky Way, and in its immediate neighborhood where the open clusters are most frequent, there are no globular clusters at all. Besides, nearly all the globular clusters are situated on one side of the sky, the

most abundant and most distant of them in the vicinity
of Sagittarius.

The most important help in investigating the star
clusters is provided by diagrams of color-magnitude relationship, such as we have drawn up earlier for the
close stars (Fig. 65). In dealing with clusters, we relate
the brightness not to spectral type but to color index,
because on the whole we can measure color index more
accurately than spectral type, and because the stars in

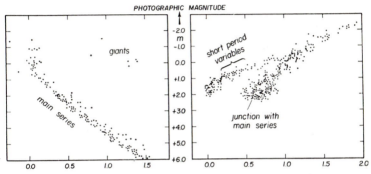

FIG. 87. Color-magnitude diagrams: luminosity and color index.
Open cluster: Praesepe. Globular cluster: Messier 92.

clusters are for the most part too faint and too close
together to provide serviceable photographs of their
spectra. Figure 87 clearly shows the typical differences
between the color-magnitude diagrams of open and those
of globular clusters (shown also in Figure 101). These
differences have a far-reaching significance, of which we
shall have more to say in our discussion of the two "star
populations."

Other Effects of Absorption

The correctness of our findings about the spatial arrangement of star clusters also depends on the effects of

absorption. Again, our computed distances will be too great if apparent brightness has been reduced by absorption. The discrepancy becomes noticeable when we compute the real size of the clusters from their dimensions on a photographic plate. Let us suppose that cluster *A* is farther away than cluster *B*. To appear equally large, *A* must have a large diameter. If there is absorption that we do not take into account, *A*'s diameter must be larger the farther away it is. Such an increase of the computed diameters with the increase of the distance has actually been encountered in the open clusters; from the rate of increase and the growth of the color index we must conclude that absorption in the region where we find open star clusters averages roughly $\frac{1}{6}$ magnitude for every 1000 light-years distance, but that it is by no means uniform.

To study absorption in greater detail, the color excess of distant B stars was investigated. These bright stars can be followed far out into space, and their spectral types can be determined at great distances. Their discoloration has been accurately measured by means of photoelectric cells. They are also called hydrogen stars (because of the conspicuous hydrogen lines in their spectra) and are all situated close to the plane of the Milky Way. Their discoloration clearly indicates the amount of absorption in different directions.

By contrast to the open clusters, the globular clusters outside of the Milky Way show no increase of diameter with increasing distance. Globular clusters include some perfectly white stars, which would be impossible if their light passed for 20,000 years or more through an absorbent and reddening dust. Hence, we must assume that the dust occurs in a space limited to our own vicinity, a space perhaps somewhat greater than that of the open star clusters. The light of the globular clusters passes through the dust only for the last short stretch of the way, and here is weakened only to an extent similar to the loss of the open clusters. For globular clusters observed close to the Milky Way, whose light passes very obliquely through the absorbent layer and is perceptibly redder, the absorption may amount to as much as 2 magnitudes. According to our table this means that these remotest of clusters may be 2½ times nearer than we thought. Now we see why we find no globular clusters in the Milky Way: clusters lying in that direction suffer the greatest possible absorption, amounting to several magnitudes, and this is enough to blot them entirely from our sight. The same holds for the still more distant spiral nebulae (p. 188) which are evenly distributed over the rest of the sky, but totally absent in an irregular zone about the Milky Way.

Among the problems of concern to modern astronomy is that of the origin of the stars. At present, many astronomers incline to the assumption that stars form out of masses of dust and gas, when great interstellar clouds collapse under certain circumstances. If this is true, stars would owe their high temperatures to the same process as we mentioned above (p. 126) in connection with the energy of the sun. But this view, it must be stressed, is still wholly hypothetical.

The Stellar System

Since we know now where absorption occurs, we can take it into account when drawing our conclusions. Perpendicular to the Milky Way, absorption is slight; hence, we can interpret Column II of our star count (p. 130) as if there were none. According to Column II, the number of stars never increases fourfold from one magnitude to the next, but at first it only doubles, and in the end it is multiplied barely 1½ times. This means that in these two directions—up and down, north and south of the galactic plane—the density of stars declines rapidly. In the same segment of space which in our vicinity contains 20 stars, we find only one star at a distance of 3000 light-years; and farther out it takes a far larger space to produce one more. We are as if in a forest that does not stop sharply, but grows gradually thinner, until at length there is no forest but rather single trees in an open field. Somewhere along the line the forest ceases to be, and in this sense we speak of a limit to our stellar system at roughly 3000 light-years on either side of the Milky Way.

On the galactic plane the limit is much more distant. If we interpreted Column I in the same way as Column II, we should arrive at some 12,000 light-years. But here we must take absorption into account, and then we never reach a limit of 5 per cent. At first, to be sure, star concentration diminishes, but it never drops below the 25 per cent of the concentration characteristic of our vicinity up to 30,000 light-years, a distance beyond which our count does not go. Thus, the stellar system to which we belong occupies a thin disk which extends farther than we have been able to see up to now. Our sun stands in the middle of the disk, but a little to the north of the central plane. Yet we need not suppose that we are the center of this system simply because the star concentration diminishes rapidly in all directions. All it means is that our sun is in the middle of a star cloud a few hundred light-years in diameter; in the other star clouds of our system, which appear to us as galactic nebulae, the concentration may be as great or greater.

A glance at the Milky Way (Fig. 88) also tells us that the structure of our stellar system cannot be so simple as to allow us to speak of a uniform decrease of star density in all directions. For we see clouds of stars that contrast more or less with one another and look very much as if they were denser clouds hanging in a thinner "air" of stars. But let us bear in mind that certain features of this cloudy structure of the Milky Way are illusions

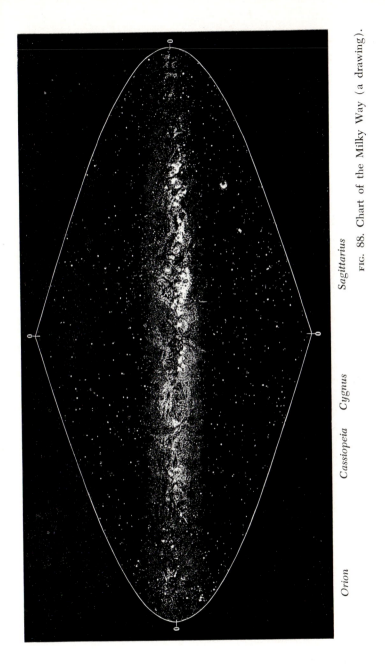

Orion   Cassiopeia   Cygnus   Sagittarius

FIG. 88. Chart of the Milky Way (a drawing).

produced by dark clouds in our vicinity. Even so, it was worthwhile for a start to lump together everything around us we could count: in this way we were able to obtain a fairly reliable picture of the extent of our system.

So far we have reached no outer limit in the Milky Way. Still we do not believe that our star system is a flat disk extending into infinity. As soon as we are able to enlarge our star counts to cover still fainter stars, we shall somewhere come upon regions where our system begins to end.

Various signs indicate that we are not at the center of our stellar system, though such a center may exist. The star counts show a higher concentration in the direction where the Milky Way shines brightest: in the region of Sagittarius which, in our northern latitudes, unfortunately rises above the horizon only briefly during the summer months. In that region we find an extraordinary number of short-period variables which, as we know, have the absolute brightness zero (p. 80). They have here an apparent brightness of 15–16; in other words, they are allowing for absorption approximately 20,000 to 30,000 light-years away. In this same region new stars appear with particular frequency. The special significance of this region strikes us also when we consider the distribution of globular clusters. Nearly all of them are situated in the same half of the sky, and they are most frequent in the zones to the north and south of the Sagittarius region of the Milky Way (in the Milky Way itself, they are made invisible by absorption). The most distant clusters lie in this direction, as does the center of the whole system of globular clusters, at a distance of roughly 30,000 light-years from the earth (Fig. 89).

Everything suggests that we may look for a center of our system—an extremely massive center, particularly rich in stars—somewhere in the region where the Milky Way touches the constellations Sagittarius, Ophiuchus,

and Scorpio. The star clouds we see there are probably
only parts of it, border zones, while the central zones
proper are presumably hidden behind the dark clouds
that here split the Milky Way into two branches. These
dark clouds are a great obstacle to the investigation of
the central parts of our stellar system. They force us to
grope along their edges to get to the center and possibly
beyond it. Only stars of great luminosity can lead us to
such distances, and we must endeavor to single them out
from the great mass of the faint stars closer by.

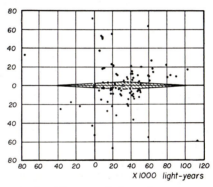

FIG. 89. Diagram of the galactic system
with the globular clusters. (× designates
the position of the sun.)

The star system that now emerges before our eyes is
much larger than we could have suspected at the beginning. We are separated from its center by a distance of
roughly 30,000 light-years, perhaps more. Yet we find
stars at distances of 30,000 light-years also on the other
side of the sky where we should most readily get to the
edge of the system. This means that there certainly are
stars as far as 60,000 light-years from the center. Hence,
the diameter of the system is probably a good deal larger
than 100,000 light-years. And the space through which
globular clusters are distributed is at least as large. For

their uniform distribution to the north and south of the Milky Way compels us to consider them as part of the galactic system, although most of them lie far outside the realm filled with stars. Nor do those remote regions seem to be otherwise entirely empty—we find in them a few short-period variables. But they are surely close to empty. The disk of galactic clouds, a few thousand light-years in thickness and perhaps a little thicker near the center, encloses almost everything that belongs to the system: billions of stars of the most various sizes, mass, luminosity; hundreds of star clusters, dust clouds, gas clouds.

The Movements Within the Stellar System

We know that this system is no dead, rigid structure. Proper motions and radial velocities have told us that the stars are all in motion, at velocities much like that of our sun (p. 136) and, it seems, without much order. We call their motion fairly disorderly—even though we have so far discovered no order whatever. For it is hard for us to imagine how a system which itself is not entirely without order could endure if all the movements of all its parts were utterly chaotic. Yet we may reflect that the molecules of gas may move in total disorder (p. 112) even while the spheres of gas float in space as seemingly stable structures.

In exactly the same way, we might conceive of the whole stellar system as in disordered motion but held together by the force of gravitation. This would not be too dangerous even for the individual stars, for there is so much space inside cosmic space—by contrast to the inside of a body of gas—that a collision could occur but rarely. By the rules of chance that apply to such "accidental" events, our sun may keep on sailing through space for several trillion years without another sun entering the region of its planetary system, and quintillions of years without a true collision. But in games of chance, there is no guarantee: our sun might remain unmolested for trillions of years, and again—theoretically—the rare chance might occur day after tomorrow. But laws of chance do give us the certainty that such catastrophes are extremely infrequent even among the billions of stars that make up our system, and have little bearing on the future of the system as a whole.

Still, we cannot reconcile ourselves to the idea that the motions of the stars are entirely unregulated. Our stellar system does not give the impression of a "gas ball"; it is not a ball at all, but a flat disk. We remember that our earth is not a perfect sphere but somewhat flattened at the poles; the diameter of the earth from pole to pole is only 7945 miles, while at the equator it measures 7972 miles. Since the polar diameter is the axis around which the earth rotates, we are certain that the rotation of the earth is the cause of its flattening. Both Jupiter and Saturn, the two large planets that rotate faster than the earth, show a greater flattening. Saturn shows something else useful for our purposes: its rings are completely flat structures lying on one plane and consisting of small bodies that move around Saturn as moons or planets move around the sun. So, too, the planets both large and small form a flat disk moving round the sun in the center. Wherever we meet such "flattenings," rotary or circular motions to produce them are present or have had a share in their origin or evolution.

All this gives us good reason to look for rotary movements in our great stellar system. To be sure, it remains a mystery how movements leading to a general rotation around an axis could ever have begun. We have no idea what part of this development falls before and what part after the formation of stellar spheres from matter that was in all likelihood irregularly diffused. But it is certain that today there can be rotary movements only around the center of the system, and that these movements are almost exactly in a plane, the plane of the Milky Way. Otherwise, the system would soon disperse upward and downward—it could not have its present flat shape.

Is the Whole System Turning?

Is it possible to demonstrate a rotation of the entire Milky Way? We can with more or less precision locate the center around which the system turns: it must be the dense nucleus that we have projected in the region of the Sagittarius cloud, roughly 30,000 light-years from us. We can even form an idea of the velocity at which we travel along our orbit. The globular clusters are helpful here. As Figure 89 shows, they do not crowd into the galactic plane nearly as closely as the vast host of stars, and we may take this as an indication that they do not fully share in the general rotation of the system. From their radial velocities, which show how our sun moves in relation to each cluster, we can remove that part which derives from the motion of the sun, just as we have earlier determined the motion of the sun in relation to the surrounding stars. We obtain a velocity of roughly 125 miles a second, in a direction exactly at right angles to the line pointing at the presumed center of the system. Actually, this velocity, calculated from the observation of 50 globular clusters, is today only of limited interest; for the observation of star velocities, and recently of the radial velocities of spiral nebulae, has yielded a greater sun velocity—almost 200 miles a second—around the center of the galactic system. Almost all of the nearby stars move at this velocity, and approximately in the same direction. Their movements in relation to the sun are only slight in comparison with the great rotary movement in which they all take part.

What happens, then, when we look at the stars that move before us in the same orbit and probably at the

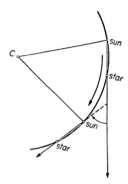

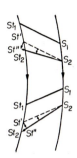

FIG. 90. Rotation of the stellar system: sun and star in
the same orbit.

FIG. 91. Rotation of the stellar system: sun and star in
different orbits.

same velocity? Figure 90 shows how our line of sight
swings around as we pass along our orbit. All the stars
that we see in this direction must be displaced in the
sky by the angle, marked with the arrow, between the
two lines of sight; this is the common proper motion we
must find if we take their positions at different times.
We know that this task is difficult. The stars do not
follow one another as nicely as we should like; they allow
themselves considerable freedom of motion, much like
the gnats in a swarm which as a whole is moving in the
same direction. Besides, the angle we are looking for is
very small despite the great velocity at which we are
moving along our orbit. It takes 300,000 years for the
line of sight to shift by the breadth of the full moon,
200 million years to complete the orbit. Thus, we cannot
expect much to become noticeable in the span of a
hundred years, and that is all the time that has gone
by since we began to measure star positions with the
necessary accuracy. Nevertheless, computation based on
all the reliable proper motions has established the rotation we have been looking for!

Let us take another look at the stars rotating beside our orbit, inside or outside of it. That they travel at the same velocity as we appears unlikely. In the solar system, the closer planets are to the sun the faster they move. We must expect similar behavior in the stellar system. Thus, while the sun (Fig. 91) moves from S_1 to S_2, a star St that is closer to the center of the system has traveled the longer segment from St_1 to St_2. A motion from St_1 to St', identical to that of the sun, we could not observe because it would not change the position of the star in relation to the sun. The only thing that strikes our attention and can be measured is the excess segment from St' to St_2, the motion of the star relative to the sun. Seen from the sun (S_2), the star changes its position in the sky as though it had moved from St' to St'', and this is what we observe as its proper motion. But at the same time its distance from the sun changes, as though it had traveled from St'' to St_2. This change in distance is, of course, continuous, and we measure it by spectroscopic observation as radial velocity.

It should be possible, on the basis of the radial velocities, to discover the law governing the relation between velocity of rotation and distance from the center, and so to ascertain whether the masses in our stellar system are more or less uniformly distributed or whether they increase greatly toward the center. For reliable inferences of this kind a larger supply of radial velocities would be desirable. To obtain clearly discernible effects, we here use giant stars at great distances, such as the long-period variables. Their absolute brightness is known. Our final computation of the rotation of the galactic system must once again take into account the troublesome phenomenon of absorption. Still, the methods just described have yielded reliable values for the velocity of rotation of the sun and its entourage, and for the direction and distance of the center of the Galaxy. The direction gives to the center of the Galaxy the same position in the sky which we have assigned to it on other grounds (p. 168): the star cloud in Sagittarius. Further support comes from the motionless calcium lines, which also indicate a rotation (p. 159).

"There Are More Things in Heaven . . ."

We must not imagine that our simple diagram expresses what really happens. It is no more than a rough sketch. True, the inner stars probably rotate at a greater velocity than the outer ones. But it is not correct to suppose that all stars at our distance from the center rotate at the same velocity. Different sorts of stars have different velocities, even in our immediate vicinity. There are stars that take almost as little part in the rotation as the globular clusters; the distance between us and them increases very quickly, and we measure radial velocities of more than 60 miles a second. But such great radial velocities we find only "behind us," not before us (these "rapid" stars are actually slow-moving ones). Thus, there are no stars that move much faster than the sun. Nor can there be, since the velocity of 200 miles a second at which the sun rotates is almost the greatest velocity possible in this orbit. If the velocity were higher, the centrifugal force would be greater than the gravitation drawing the sun inward. Stars with such velocities cannot be held—they leave the stellar system forever.

Even the host of stars around us, which on the whole moves at the same high velocity as the sun, does not exactly keep step. Some clusters of stars, such as Praesepe (the Manger) or the Hyades, seem to move separately at a uniform velocity in a direction cutting across the general movement. In reality their orbit is merely at a slight angle to the orbit of the sun. Figure 92, for simplicity's sake, assumes that sun and star cluster have come together at one point, and then separated. There

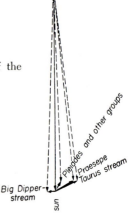

FIG. 92. Real and apparent motion of the sun and nearby stars and star groups.

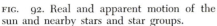

Big Dipper stream

are also groups of stars wandering in unison that we do not see as clusters because we are in the midst of them. Five bright stars of the Big Dipper, Sirius, the second brightest star in Auriga, the brightest star in Corona Borealis, Beta Eridani, and many fainter stars in other parts of the sky—these form such a "stream" of stars, whose members we can recognize only by the fact that their motions in space are parallel and that their proper motions point from all different directions in the sky toward a single goal.

But the other stars, too, which do not belong to a cluster or stream, do not move along in parallel orbits either. If they did, nearby stars would scarcely change their positions in relation to us; we should observe no radial velocity or proper motion for them. And in that case we should never have discovered the sun's motion in relation to the totality of the stars around it. What we see from where we stand is a complex tangle of motions. Since all these observed motions of 10, 15, or 20 miles a second are small in comparison with the rotary motion of 200 miles a second, none of them means anything more than a greater or lesser deviation from the direction of the circular orbit. But even that is highly significant: it means that stars which are now together are slowly separating. It may also mean that concentrations of stars are not permanent.

These observations are supported by observations of "associations" of stars, that is, groups of stars of the same type that are not close together in space but occur mixed in among the other stars. These associations may be the remnants of a star cluster that has scattered. For example, it has been found that the brighter O and B stars often form loose associations in the sky. Recent measurements of the proper motions of an association of 17 O and B stars in Perseus have shown that they all seem to be moving away from the same center. If their velocity has remained unchanged, they must have left this center 1.3 million years ago. Did this star group actually form at that time? Our theories of star structure have led us to believe that these stars cannot be much older than a few million years.

We must not forget to accompany each of our conclusions with a cautious "perhaps." Every conception we have formed or can form is an attempt to construe what we observe as part of a great process whose totality is hidden from us. But the part of it that we can survey is so small in point of space, so brief in point of time compared to the whole that only our trust in the uniformity of the physical process throughout the universe supports our hope of learning something about the whole.

II. THE GREATER UNIVERSE

We are still busy trying to make out the essential structure of our stellar system and to interpret our observations in this world of the stars. But even now a new, serious question compels our attention: is this "the universe"? We are already in a position to say, no, even this is only a part, a very small part of the universe. We do not say so because our galactic world does not seem grand enough, nor for the more serious reason that it is hard for us to conceive of a measurable world embedded in nothingness—we say so simply and concretely because we see things in the sky that do not belong to the world with which we have been dealing up to now. Figures 15

FIG. 93. A handsome spiral in the Big Dipper (39-inch reflector of the Hamburg Observatory).

and 93 show some of these extragalactic objects. They are known as spiral nebulae, or simply spirals. Two "arms" radiate from opposite sides of a thick nucleus and lie in spiral coils around it. The arms of the spirals cannot always be recognized so clearly; often they are more irregular and blurred. Only spirals which we see from above or below have this distinctive shape. Much more frequently we see them obliquely from one side (Fig. 94), and many of them we see along the plane in

FIG. 94. A spiral in the Big Dipper seen from another angle (39-inch reflector of the Hamburg Observatory).

FIG. 95. Spiral in Coma Berenices seen from the side (100-inch reflector of the Mt. Wilson Observatory).

which the spiral arms wind around the nucleus (Fig. 95).

Not all of the extragalactic nebulae are proper spirals. Even among the larger and nearer ones, there are nebulae which even in the most powerful telescopes reveal no spiral structure (Fig. 96). Taking into account various characteristics such as size, total brightness, and spectrum, we can establish a sequence of extragalactic nebulae which leads from the structureless circular and

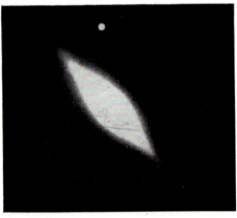

FIG. 96. Spindle-shaped spiral nebula in Sextans (photograph of the Mt. Wilson Observatory).

elliptical nebulae to the dense spirals and on to the loose spirals, and which might possibly represent a progressive development. There are utterly irregular nebulae (a small percentage of the total number), including the nearby Magellanic Clouds (Fig. 45), that do not fit into this sequence.

The Spirals Are Stellar Systems

As early as 200 years ago, "nebulous spots" were regarded as distant stellar systems, but only 30 years ago they were still thought to be no more than a few thousand light-years away. Certainty was attained only when the great American telescopes made it possible to take photographs on which individual stars could be distinguished at least in the outer parts of the larger spirals. It now was clear that the spirals are not mists but star clusters or star systems, as had previously been conjectured on the strength of their continuous spectra with many absorption lines.

A Hundred Million Galaxies

The outer star systems are tremendously numerous. Whenever a new, larger telescope is put in use vast numbers of new nebulae appear in the photographs. We have been forced to conclude that, far as we have penetrated into space, we have not yet reached the limit of the universe and its stellar systems. Computations from fields actually observed with the 100-inch reflector of Mt. Wilson Observatory,—up to 1948 the most powerful telescope in the world—indicate the existence, in the entire sky, of some 100 million stellar systems. Outside of the Milky Way, the fainter objects include more nebulae than stars. And even the 200-inch reflector cannot be expected to reach the limit of the universe.

Looking at this "universe of universes," we want to

know two things. How big is it? Are its stellar systems similar to our own in nature and in size?

As we study pictures of one of the larger spirals, we can easily imagine that an observer on one of the stars in its interior would see something very similar to our sky: the bright and faint stars of the immediate vicinity, farther on a luminous ring of stars not individually distinguishable and often condensed into star clouds such as we see in our Milky Way. Even those dark masses of dust that have given us so much trouble in the investigation of our system are not lacking, as the pictures of nearly all the spirals we see sideways (Fig. 95) make clear. And this is not all: even globular clusters of tens or hundreds of thousands of stars, which could be regarded as a peculiarity of our system, are found in many extragalactic nebulae.

How Far Away Are the Spiral Nebulae?

In order to find out whether these stellar systems are roughly similar to our own in size, we must know their distances. Only then can we compute their real size from their apparent extension in the sky. We have already found out (in dealing with globular clusters, for example) that it is difficult to measure the distance of such remote objects. The difficulties are almost insuperable. For such distances the measurement of any sort of parallax is entirely out of the question, and there remains only one possibility: we must find stars whose real brightness we know, and measure their apparent brightness. The difference between the two gives us their distance (p. 83), unless their light has been so weakened on its long journey that they appear too faint and hence too distant.

In a few of the closer spirals, stars of Cepheid variable type (p. 79) have helped us to a fairly accurate knowledge of their distance. Forty such variables have been distinguished in the great Andromeda nebula and 35 in

FIG. 97. Corner of the great spiral in Andromeda–see Fig. 100 (100-inch reflector of the Mt. Wilson Observatory).

the Triangulum nebula. These two great spirals have been found to be almost equally distant—some 1,400,000 light-years away. They are far removed from our stellar system, whose diameter we have estimated at 100,000 light-years.

In the other spirals we unfortunately know no Cepheid variables. But in some dozen spirals we have found novae (Fig. 98) which even grow a little brighter than the Cepheids. In the Andromeda nebula alone, more than 100 have been found within 50 years (as against 90 so far in our own system). Observation of the brightness of the novae in Andromeda, together with the distance that we already know, gives us a reliable mean value for the luminosity attained by novae in their period of maximum brightness. Their apparent brightness in other spirals gives us an indication, though unfortunately a very vague one, of their distance. Apart from the Andromeda nebula, we have so far found only one or two novae in each

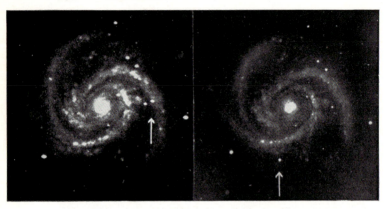

FIG. 98. Two photographs of the same spiral nebula, taken in 1901 and 1914. Each photograph shows a star which is lacking in the other (photographs of the Lick Observatory).

spiral, and we cannot assume that every nova is exactly at its average luminosity. We must therefore choose another bridge to advance from the nebulae whose distances are known to the more distant ones. This bridge will be the brightest stars—provided we can distinguish individual stars at all. There are theoretical reasons for supposing that there is a limit to the brightness a star can attain. Now our observation shows that the three or four brightest stars, both in the galactic system and in the nearer extragalactic systems (stars of the O and B types), have always approximately the same brightness, somewhat greater than that of the novae. Hence, where stars can be distinguished in a nebula, we can compute its distance by measuring the brightness of its brightest stars.

Since in the distant nebulae the stars are exceedingly faint, just barely recognizable (twentieth and twenty-first magnitudes), it is extremely difficult to measure their brightness with the necessary accuracy. We must further bear in mind that the maximum brightness on which our computations are based is not necessarily attained in every single stellar system, for maximum brightness has been computed as an average, and is valid only for a large number of nebulae lumped together. Nature, fortunately, has chosen to come to our aid. There exist *nebular clusters*, groups of 3 or 10 or 20 nebulae, as well as true clusters containing several hundred, even several thousand nebulae (Fig. 99). In one of these clusters, apparently the nearest, situated in Virgo, a large number of spirals have been singled out. With the help of their brightest stars, the cluster as a whole has been quite reliably computed to be 14 million light-years distant. All other nebular clusters, some 20 of which are now known, are too far for us to distinguish stars in them. We

FIG. 99. A field of the sky showing a large number of spiral and spherical nebulae (39-inch reflector of the Hamburg Observatory).

could do so only in the very rare case of a supernova, for a supernova is roughly 8 magnitudes brighter than the normally brightest stars and temporarily emits as much light as the whole stellar system to which it belongs.

The great number of the nebulae that make up these nebular clusters provides us with another possibility—using statistics. We can determine the brightness of the nebulae themselves as well as the distribution of individual brightnesses around their mean value. If we find the same distribution in the different clusters, it becomes highly probable that the average brightnesses correspond to the same luminosity and therefore give us relative distances. By means of a cluster distance determined in some other way—and this is provided by the Virgo cluster—we arrive at the distances of the nebular clusters, the most distant objects we know.

Here, as we have seen, we can no longer simply measure and calculate. We are reduced to groping our way. What method to choose in each case can be decided only by the "instinct" of the astronomer who has a thorough command of all available data.

Our Place in the Stellar Systems

The distances so determined tell us this: we belong to a group of star systems that are relatively close together. Fifteen systems have so far been reliably assigned to this group: our own, with the Large and the Small Magellanic Cloud at a distance of 150,000 light-years (which is no farther than the more distant globular clusters of our own system); the great Andromeda nebula (Messier 31) with its two smaller elliptical companions (Messier 32 and NGC 205), at a distance of 1,400,000 light-years (Fig. 100); the open spiral in Triangulum (Messier 33), which is also some 1,400,000 light-years distant from us, but less than 40,000 light-years from the Andromeda nebula; and the other systems in the table.

At distances of 8 million light-years we encounter the first of the "external" nebulae, some of them single, others in groups or clusters that seem to occupy all the space accessible to our investigation. The faintest nebulae that can be recognized on the plates of the Mt. Palomar

FIG. 100. Celestial field with the great Andromeda nebula and its two companions, directly below and to the upper right of the nucleus (14-inch Schmidt telescope of the Hamburg Observatory).

reflector must be assigned a distance of approximately 2 billion light-years. Since the time when the light rays by which we see these star systems today left their source, our sun has presumably circled 10 times around the nucleus of our stellar system (p. 172), but our earth already existed in approximately its present form (p.

127). At first sight the distribution of the nebulae seems very uneven; they are totally lacking, for example, in the zone of the Milky Way. The reason, we recall, from our study of the globular clusters, is that their light has been absorbed by the dark dust masses of our system (p. 164). Considering everything we know on the subject, we reach the conclusion that cosmic space is by and large populated evenly with stellar systems.

The Local Group of the Star Systems

NAME	DISTANCE (LIGHT-YEARS)	TYPE	ABSOLUTE MAGNITUDE
Milky Way	...	spiral	−19.7
Messier 31	1,400,000	spiral	−19.4
Messier 33	1,500,000	spiral	−17.3
Great Magellanic Cloud	140,000	irregular	−17.6
Small Magellanic Cloud	150,000	irregular	−16.4
NGC 205	1,400,000	elliptical	−14.9
Messier 32	1,400,000	elliptical	−14.9
NGC 6822	1,000,000	irregular	−13.8
NGC 185	1,200,000	elliptical	−13.7
IC 1613	1,500,000	irregular	−13.7
NGC 147	1,200,000	elliptical	−13.4
Fornax System	900,000	elliptical	−13.6
Sculptor System	500,000	elliptical	−12.1
Nameless 1	1,300,000	elliptical	...
Nameless 2	1,300,000	elliptical	...

Are all the stellar systems of the same kind and size as ours? We have seen that there are different kinds representing, perhaps, different stages of development. The nebulae seem to grow larger as they develop from an elliptical to a loose spiral form. Our galactic system seems to be comparable to the intermediate form, the looser spirals. They exhibit all the features that are familiar to us from our own system: stars of all sorts, open and globular clusters, gas clouds, and dust clouds. But when we compute their true size from their distance and apparent size, most of them prove to be smaller than 20,000 light-years, and even for the seemingly enormous Andromeda nebula the outlines visible on photographic plates give us a diameter of only 80,000 light-years.

We must bear in mind that our estimates of our system and of the extragalactic systems are based on different characteristics. The highest figure for the diameter of our system, roughly 200,000 light-years, circumscribes the zone in which globular clusters are present. But in dealing with external systems, we set an outer limit at those regions whose star population is still abundant enough to be visible on our photographic plates; we have no way of knowing what portion of the system we neglect by this method. In the Andromeda nebula, however, we can discern globular clusters far outside the visible spiral, and more recently, improved photometric observation has almost doubled our measurement of the nebular surface. Thus, the galactic system and the Andromeda nebula are stellar systems of similar size.

Two Types of "Population" in the Stellar Systems

The color-magnitude diagrams of the open star clusters and of the globular clusters show characteristic differences (p. 163). The stars in our vicinity have the same diagrams as the open clusters. To what extent the differences apply to the fainter stars is something we do not know, for in the globular clusters we can no longer examine fainter stars singly for brightness and color. On the strength of observations of the nucleus of the Andromeda nebula, which was first broken up into individual stars in 1944, astronomers concluded that the nuclei of spiral nebulae had probably the same color-magnitude diagrams as the globular clusters. This assumption was supported by the appearance of numerous variables with short periods (less than one day; these stars are known as "cluster variables") both in globular clusters and in the Sagittarius cloud which we regard as the center of our Galaxy.

These two types of color-magnitude diagrams have led to a distinction between two "populations" among the stars. Population I comprises: our vicinity, the open star clusters, the arms of spiral nebulae. Population I is

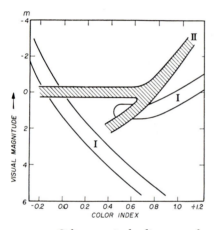

FIG. 101. Color-magnitude diagrams of Populations I and II.

marked by the occurrence of O and B stars, long-period variables, and interstellar matter such as hydrogen. Since interstellar matter often takes the form of clouds, this population is also known as the "cloud population." Population II, also called "nuclear population," is free of interstellar matter and includes red giants and short-period variables.

The distinction is still somewhat artificial. In reality, these populations hardly exist in pure form, nor can any individual star be assigned to one or the other population. It may be that the swiftly moving stars (p. 175), with their elongated orbits around the center of the Galaxy (and perhaps running partly through the nucleus), are messengers from the nucleus population. This question is still unsettled.

The Spiral Structure of the Stellar Systems

So far we have had no time to wonder at the spiral form of the nebulae, surprising though it is. Why is it that the stellar systems, at what we assume to be their later development, have a spiral structure? It seems certain that the reason must be sought in the forms of motion prevailing in the different periods. Various hypotheses have been advanced.

Theoretically, it is possible that when a rotating mass of gas exceeds a certain velocity of rotation, matter pours forth at two opposite points on its equator. The formation of the solar system out of the sun may have been a process of this sort on a smaller scale. But about the subsequent distribution and motion of matter opinions may still differ widely, in the total absence of observations on which to base a judgment. Rotation surely occurs everywhere. We have established it in the galactic system, and spectroscopic observation has even proved that a few of the spirals rotate. For example, in measuring the velocity of the Andromeda nebula at different points along its longest diameter, we found that one-half of it is moving toward us, the other away from us. To begin with, velocity of rotation increases from the core on out— only far outside, where star concentration has greatly decreased, may this trend be reversed. These observations allow an estimate of the distribution of masses within a spiral nebula, as well as of its total mass (stars and interstellar matter together). We arrive at figures between roughly 2 billion and 2 hundred billion times the mass of the sun.

To understand the nature of the spiral nebulae, we

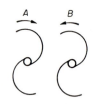

FIG. 102. Two possible directions of rotation for spiral nebulae.

must know which way the spirals are turning: do the ends trail behind, as in a pinwheel, or do they lead (*A* and *B* in Figure 102)? Some spirals are so tilted that we can measure both velocity and direction of rotation, and distinguish the shape of the spiral arms. But there are still two possibilities: for we still do not know which of the two halves on either side of the longest diameter is closer to us. Not until we know this can we determine the spirals' direction. We seek the answer in the effect of absorbing clouds present in the spiral arms, clouds that are partly projected against the nucleus. Most astronomers have adopted hypothesis *A*—rotation like a pinwheel. General agreement, however, can be reached only by the most thorough and accurate photometric investigations. Now that we know that the Galaxy is a spiral nebula, which we provisionally assume to rotate like a pinwheel, there is nothing to prevent us from accepting hypothesis *A* in Figure 102 for all spiral nebulae.

Our Galaxy Is a Spiral Nebula

That our galaxy is a spiral nebula has been asserted often, and on likely grounds. But conclusive proof had not been offered until the most recent investigations, using both radio astronomy and the methods of classical astronomy.

Radio astronomy is based on a theoretical assumption about the behavior of the highly attenuated hydrogen which is characteristic of spiral arms: to wit, that it emits a radiation with a wave length of 8.2 inches, which falls within the segment of wave lengths where modern radar apparatus operates. With the help of radar it has recently been possible to demonstrate that a radiation of this sort actually does reach us from the depths of cosmic space. It is not appreciably obstructed by interstellar matter or by the clouds or our atmosphere. Highly re-fined measurements have made it possible to compute the velocities and distances of these hydrogen clouds. Figure 103 shows one of the first results of these investigations. The science of radio astronomy, young as it is, has made a decisive discovery.

The distance of galactic objects containing incandes-

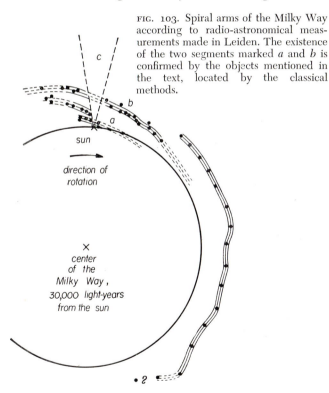

FIG. 103. Spiral arms of the Milky Way according to radio-astronomical measurements made in Leiden. The existence of the two segments marked *a* and *b* is confirmed by the objects mentioned in the text, located by the classical methods.

sun

direction of
rotation

×
center
of the
Milky Way,
30,000 light-years
from the sun

cent hydrogen has been established by classical methods. Incandescent hydrogen is shown in the spectrum by a bright red line (Fig. 58, H_a). As shown in Figure 103, such objects containing incandescent hydrogen form two rows *a* and *b* in the Galaxy, which may be interpreted as segments of spiral arms. The general rotation round the center of the galactic system is clockwise; from the inclination of the spiral arms we conclude that the spiral rotates like a pinwheel.

The figure does not include those parts of the Milky Way that are not visible in Leiden. But the same problem is being studied in our Southern Hemisphere. In a few years, despite the great technical difficulty of such investigations, we shall no doubt have a general picture of the spiral arms of the Galaxy. Certain segments of the hydrogen clouds, however, cannot be observed (for example, *c* in Figure 103) because here the hydrogen is moving in the same direction as the sun.

Where Are the Nebulae Going?

Even before the spectrograph made it possible to determine rotation and with it differences of motion, there had been measurements of the radial velocity of the nuclei of some nebulae, and with it the velocity of each nebula as a whole. Here the line displacements are large, nearly always much larger than for stars. But the blurred and flat appearance of the nebulae made it very difficult to observe fainter objects. Only very recently has it become possible to extend measurements to include faint nebulae, and to increase the number of known radial velocities from several dozen to a few hundred.

The Andromeda nebula is approaching us at a velocity of 135 miles a second, the Triangulum nebula at 200 miles, and there is one of the smaller nebulae in our group approaching us at 100 miles a second. But these are almost the only negative velocities that occur, and even they are almost wholly a reflection of our own motion, the motion of the sun around the nucleus of the Galaxy. All other nebular velocities have proved to be positive, even those of the brighter nebulae which were at first the only ones accessible to measurement, and the velocities become progressively larger as the nebulae become fainter and more distant.

In Figure 104 the nebulae whose distances have been determined with the help of stars, and whose radial velocities have been measured, are designated by points. The points are farther to the right of the vertical zero line in proportion as the nebulae are more distant, and farther above the horizontal zero line in proportion as their positive radial velocities are greater, that is, in proportion as the nebulae move away from us more and more rapidly. The effect of the sun's motion has already been eliminated in this figure. The members of our group that would fall next to the zero point are not shown; the Virgo cluster is represented by a cross. The diagram shows beyond the possibility of a doubt that radial velocity increases with increasing distance; but the existence of so interesting a relation has become more and more certain with the progress of photometric and spectrographic observation. The nebular clusters in particular

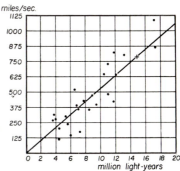

FIG. 104. The remarkable connection between radial velocity and distance of the spiral nebulae.

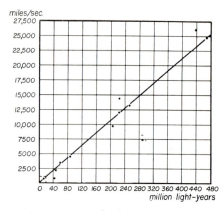

FIG. 105. A straight line of great significance.

provide reliable indices, since in them several (from 5 to 30) velocities are available for the same distance. Figure 105 shows on a small scale all observations up to 25,000 miles a second. Measurements of distant nebulae with nuclei bright enough for observation have shown no deviations from the straight line up to velocities of more than 40,000 miles a second. Only the most recent measurements—of velocities up to almost 100,000 miles a second, about half the speed of light—seem to indicate some deviation.

The Riddle of the Universe

We must attempt to understand what this relation may mean. At first the discovery that all other stellar systems are moving away from us arouses our distrust. It seems to make us once again the center of the world. But a world whose parts are pushing outward at velocities increasing with their distance from the center, would look the same from any point within it: the scale of distance is changing throughout. A toy balloon may serve as an example. We make marks on it for the spiral nebulae. Now if we blow the balloon up a little more, all points grow farther apart. Seen from any one point on the balloon, all other points are moving away at velocities that grow larger as the points are more distant from our place of observation. We seem to be living in a universe that is flying apart.

We might explain this state of our universe by a simple assumption. If at any point in the past all matter in the universe had been united in one place and forced apart by an explosion from within, those of its parts that were hurled outward with the greatest velocities would, obviously, have today reached the greatest distances. This notion may at first seem trivial. But as it was carefully worked out it provided hopeful suggestions for an understanding of the processes involved in the "creation" of the world. Today scientists are attempting to hold this "primordial explosion" responsible even for the observed frequency of the chemical elements. If we assume the stellar systems to have retained their velocities from the very beginning, we can easily figure out how many years they have taken to arrive at their present positions. In this way we arrive at an "age" for the universe of several billion years. This length of time seems also to be the limit of the age of rock formations on the earth and of the meteors that have fallen upon the earth. We must not draw hasty conclusions about the real age of the universe.

There is no doubt that the discovery of the positive velocities of the nebulae must influence all our thinking about the nature and development of the universe. Before we go any further, therefore, it will be well to review once more our observations and make sure that they definitely point to an expanding universe of stellar systems. The displacements in the spectral lines are there. Particularly in spectrographic observations, they are un-

Radial
velocity
0 miles/sec.

−116

+3000

+4200

+12,500

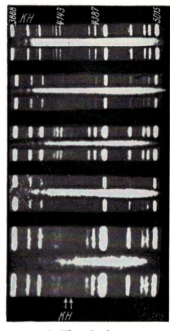

FIG. 106. The displacement, increasing with distance, of the spectrum lines of the spiral nebulae. Uppermost spectrum: diffuse sunlight. Comparison spectra: helium. KH: the ultraviolet calcium lines (photographs of the Mount Wilson Observatory).

mistakable. The displacement of the total radiation toward the longer wave lengths is so great for the more distant nebulae that even the ultraviolet light moves into the visible zone (Fig. 106). Even the radio astronomers have recently found the line displacement for radiation from a distant spiral—a particularly important discovery! The only remaining question is whether this displacement toward the red is a consequence of motions. There

are other factors that affect the wave lengths of light—
electric and magnetic forces, pressure, and gravitation,
for example—but we can conceive of no conditions under
which all these factors could exert such great effects. For
the present we have only the alternative of attributing
these displacements toward red to a still unknown cause
or else of believing in the great motions.

Our efforts to interpret our observations of the star
systems must not let us forget that our modes of thought
have been shaped by our experience of our immediate
surroundings and that they may have to be modified to
fit a new and larger cosmos. In speaking of the motions
of the nebulae (p. 197), we should have mentioned that
the universe is never as it seems: the Andromeda nebula,
for example, appears to us in the light it emitted 1,400,000
years ago and the most distant nebula we see in their
state of more than 2 billion years ago. (The latest figures
indicate that the universe is 5 billion years old.)

It is significant that the measurement of the color indices of distant spiral nebulae has for the most part
yielded values higher than those for nebulae in the
vicinity of our Galaxy. Only part of this "reddening" can
be explained by the displacement of the spectrum toward
the red. One attempt to account for the excess reddening
is the hypothesis that at the time when the light emanated from the distant systems their composition was
different, that, for example, there were then more red
giants in such a system than there are today.

It is particularly significant that the observed velocities
of nebulae come closer and closer to the speed of light
(186,000 miles a second), upon the propagation of which
our whole knowledge of space and time and velocities
depends. The greatest velocities measured thus far for
nebulae of known distance amount to one-fifth the speed
of light, but if the relation between distance and velocity
remains unchanged we must assign velocities of one-

fourth or one-third the speed of light to the most remote nebulae visible to us. The reflection that we might be the inhabitants of a stellar system shooting through space at the full speed of light and that, if this be true, we have no knowledge at all of whatever lies behind us, drives home to us that we are approaching the limits of what knowledge we can attain, and that we may no longer blindly trust our powers of reasoning or the time-honored methods of physics. Physical science has run into such limits when it prepared to look inside the atoms that had hitherto been regarded as the basic components of our physical world. Here, in the realm of the very small, a good deal happens that does not fit in with our habits of thought. It is quite possible that similar experiences await us in the realm of the very large.

But to accept the unintelligible is contrary to the fundamental attitude of scientific research. The true scientist will check his observations over and over again, and when they permit of no further doubt he will proceed to change his basic concepts and his basic principles in such a way that what was previously unintelligible now becomes comprehensible and fits into our picture of the world. Various attempts have already been made to relate the world of the very small in this way to the world of the very large. We must leave it to the future to form a definitive picture of what looks to us now like a universe in process of dissolution.

INDEX